CW00676993

TREES · OF · SOUTH INDIA

TREES
· OF ·
SOUTH
INDIA

NATIVE TREES AND SHRUBS
OF THE SOUTH INDIAN PLAINS
AND HILLOCKS

TREE IDENTIFICATION BOOK
Auroville Botanical Gardens

HarperCollins *Publishers* India

First published in India by HarperCollins *Publishers* 2024
Building No 10, Tower A, 4th Floor, DLF Cyber City, Phase II,
Gurugram – 122002
www.harpercollins.co.in

2 4 6 8 10 9 7 5 3 1

P-ISBN: 978-93-5699-921-3
E-ISBN: 978-93-5489-791-7

Cover and book design by Bhavana

Printed and bound at
Replika Press Pvt. Ltd.

CONTENTS

FOREWORD

There's something about Auroville that seems to attract intrepid, committed people who do wonderfully imaginative things together. One locus of such work has been the environment, which must have been forbiddingly grim in the 1970s when a small group of Aurovilians first put spade to earth. Over the years, they managed to transform a barren, eroded dustbowl into a green forested land which, in many ways, was like a first lesson for everyone else about how to bring back not just any old forest but an endangered native ecosystem that was little known at the time and could easily have slipped into oblivion: the Tropical Dry Evergreen Forests of the Coromandel Coast.

Aka TDEF.

Auroville's Botanical Gardens were founded in the year 2000 and was followed, almost in perfect phase, by a virtual herbarium of the plants of the TDEF, and now this tree identification book that you hold in your hands. With *Trees of South India*, Auroville Botanical Gardens join a small but exceptional crew of amateur naturalists and plant explorers who have created field guides in recent years consciously aimed at ordinary people. Goodbye Botanical Survey of India and its badly written, lazily compiled, herbarium-based, mostly incomprehensible Floras!

What stands out is that the authors of all these new field guides tend not to be trained botanists or biologists but enthusiasts who want to reach out and share their excitement and love of plants and creatures with a wider catchment of readers. And for this reason, their writing and descriptions are invariably direct, and the keys and layouts well thought out and disarmingly simple to use.

This recent explosion of field guides is by no means limited to trees and wildflowers—in the last 5 years alone, I can think of several guides to butterflies and moths, dragonflies, birds, reptiles and frogs that deliberately set out to participate in this joyful spirit of 'citizen science'. True, there are still realms to cover—fish, fungi and several major phyla of invertebrates spring to mind—but I can't help feeling we are in the midst of a whole new surge of exploration of the natural world around us.

Is this just happenstance?

Or does it have anything to do with a growing sense that the natural world, especially in India, is under siege and shrinking fast?

I lean towards this view. The institutions that we ought to be able to trust to protect our wildlands and wildlife are proving to be inadequate for the task. We are seeing a steady, deliberate hollowing out of the laws and procedures that are meant to protect the natural environment. Very little of it is simply collateral damage—more like a knowing, deliberate strategy to subjugate the interests of the environment to industry and infrastructure. Nature hardly figures in the calculus of today's policy options.

It may be difficult today to be sanguine about the future of the natural environment in India. But when you see books like *Trees of South India*, it gives you hope and allows you to imagine that maybe, somehow, we will be able to pull back from the brink.

Pradip Krishen
January 2022

AUTHOR'S NOTE

Trees, for me, are like best friends. They listen and don't interrupt. They have opinions, but don't push them on you. They only answer when you are ready to listen and open to hearing what they have to say, and if you just want to be quiet and go for a walk, they keep the space, watch over you and don't interfere. Of course, they love to surprise you with little gifts or unexpected treasures, and once in a while, they are happy to introduce you to their friends, the ones that they live with, who sit in the branches or drink from their flowers.

But I think, without doubt, the best thing about trees is that you can bump into them in the most unexpected of places and at that moment of recognition, there is happiness in reconnecting with a familiar old friend. Someone who you can pick up with as if you were last chatting yesterday, even though you haven't seen each other for years.

As you can imagine, my relationship with trees is deep and long lasting. I grew up in a village in the south of England that was surrounded by forests. I would wander for hours amongst the trees, at first with my parents, but as I grew older, I would take off alone and explore the area, wandering for the entire day, discovering ways that were often little used by other people. For me, the names of the trees were second nature; there was never a point in time that I had to learn them, they were just there. However, when I came to India and settled in Auroville, I had to begin anew amongst a landscape that was completely unfamiliar. I arrived at the beginning of the nineties, fresh from graduating university where I had studied forestry and ecology.

I had been drawn to Auroville by the stories of regenerating a wasteland, a tale that had begun twenty years previously as people from all over the world had come to start an experiment in Human Unity.

When I arrived, I was amazed by the dedication and commitment of the foresters within the community. Many of them had been around since the early years and had devoted the best parts of their lives to planting trees and protecting them. Amongst this group, there was a small number of individuals who were starting to systematically research the native forests of the area. It was the perfect opportunity for me, and I happily joined them on their journey. We began to explore the forest remnants and put the parts of the puzzle together.

Of course, learning the names of the trees and shrubs was a fundamental first step. We were lucky as there was an amazing botanist by the name of Father Mathews based in Trichy who was just completing a decade-long project to publish a flora of the Tamil Nadu Carnatic. Geographically, Auroville lies a little to the north of this region; however, the majority of our species were covered by his work. Over time, we were able to develop a personal relationship with him and he joined us a few times on our explorations.

However, it was a challenge. His book was a traditional flora with binomial keys, focusing on flowers as the primary means of identification and filled with botanical jargon to describe the plants. I am sure alone I would have lacked the patience to work systematically, but fortunately,

we were a group, each with our own skills. Together, over a number of years, we managed to wade through the technical terms, learning as we went, and come up with the names of the plants we held in our hands.

At the same time as familiarizing ourselves with the plants, we were also collecting the seeds, learning how to propagate them and grow them in our nurseries, with the aim of planting the native species as an understorey to the Auroville forests, and it was at this point that we began on the journey which has led to the creation of this book. As we approached the different land stewards of the forest areas, encouraging them to plant these new trees and shrubs, we had to pass on our hard-won knowledge and teach them the names, so that they in turn would be able to understand the different ecological information associated with individual species and plant them within the right niches in the forests. For within the group of trees and shrubs we had discovered, there were some better adapted to the shade, others more suited to poor soils, and others that were able to withstand partial waterlogging as they were naturally found alongside rivers and waterbodies.

Our first attempt was a book we called the *Tree Planters Guide to the TDEF*. We borrowed, with permission, illustrations from Father Mathew's Flora and created a spiral bound volume that held information on around 120 species of trees we were by then growing in our nurseries. As the years went by, we became more tech-savvy, and created websites that disseminated the information and held digital photos of the plants, such as *http://auroville-tdef.info/* and later on *https://www.plantekey.com/* and *https://aurovilleherbarium.org/*.

However, although we can be dazzled and impressed by the way information is instantly accessible via the internet, a book still has extraordinary value. It is something that has the power to inspire and encourage people to educate themselves, either through an intensive period of serious study or by occasionally picking it up and leafing through the pages. Over the past few years, a number of amazing books have been published, that have satisfied a yearning amongst people to learn more about the trees around them, and this drew us towards the idea of publishing a field guide for the trees and shrubs that are by now so familiar to us.

So, we are happy to present this field book, not the work of one person, but a wide group of individuals who all have a passion for the natural world. Some of the photos in this book were taken over 25 years ago, on our initial surveys, and others very recently as we still discover new species in the region unknown to us before. It is a journey that will continue, and that hopefully more people will join and carry further into the future, both with respect to identifying and studying the plant, as well as protecting the existing, and creating new, forests where the species can thrive.

Paul Blanchflower

SCOPE OF THE BOOK

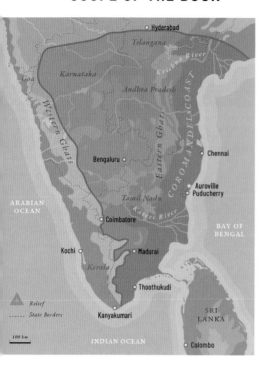

This book covers the native trees and shrubs found growing from the Coromandel Coast of South India to the lower reaches of the Western Ghats and on the hillocks of the Eastern Ghats to an altitude of around 1000 metres. Geographically, this range covers the states of Tamil Nadu, Andhra Pradesh, Telangana, Karnataka and, to some extent, Odisha.

This region is climatically diverse, with variations in the strengths of the SW and NW monsoons for different regions, as well as the rain shadow effects of the Western Ghats and Sri Lanka, ensuring that the average annual rainfalls vary from as low as 600 mm in some interior locations up to around 1500 mm along the coast belt. The presence or absence of species is clearly related to these patterns and other environmental parameters such as max temperatures, presence or absence of dew fall, soil types and altitude. This geographical distribution of species around the region is of immense interest and is the subject of ongoing research by the team at the Auroville Botanical Gardens, which will have added significance as we move into a period of climate change brought on by the increase in CO_2 in the atmosphere. Native plants will have a major role to play in the future, as they have built-in resilience to the fluctuations inherent in our tropical climate, but the more we understand about their ecology, the better we will be able to make intelligent choices when planting.

The two main forest types covered are the Tropical Dry Evergreen Forest and the Dry Deciduous Forest. There is no clear demarcation of species within each forest type, for we find some of the evergreen species in the areas we consider to be Dry Deciduous Forest, and the opposite is also true, for we find the deciduous species in the stands of Tropical Dry Evergreen Forest. However, there are clearly two different ecosystems in existence as, close to the coast, the evergreen species is predominant. The leaves of these species are often at first glance difficult to distinguish; the simple, waxy, relatively small leaf seems to be the most stable evolutionary answer to survival and reproduction in this specific region. However, on closer examination, some of the leaves release strong aromas when crushed, others have indentations at the tip, and the venation patterns on the underside also help to distinguish certain species. And it is also worth noting that some of the leaves are compound, made up of 3, 5 or 7 leaflets, even though when handling them for the first time, this may not seem obvious.

Why some species are deciduous and others evergreen is a question that does not seem to have a definitive answer, and, indeed, may well be the result of multiple environmental factors. Water loss is often the primary factor, for we can observe that leaf or leaflet size decreases as the arid conditions become more extreme, and the decision to go deciduous also means that water loss is easier to control through the closing of the leaf scar. However, there are a number of deciduous species that happily inhabit other monsoon regions with high average annual rainfalls. So that leads us to the understanding that the length of the dry season and predictability of the onset of the monsoon also play an important factor. For when we arrive in the coastal zones, the predictability of the summer rains onset is more erratic. We can see that the deciduous strategy is associated with a clear start to the rainy season, where the trees and shrubs know that this is the one and only time growth will be possible, so it is time to utilize the stored resources from last year in one growth spurt, and then settle down to the job of flower, fruit and seed production. In the areas of erratic rainfall, the evergreen species will have the advantage as they will grow a little bit each time the rains come, and then wait to see if more moisture is forthcoming in subsequent days. Once again, this is a subject of interest and something that the Auroville team is actively researching at the present time.

With respect to species not to be found within the covers of this book, we have omitted the specialized trees and shrubs of the mangroves, as they have been extensively covered in other publications and are part of a very distinctive and geographically isolated ecosystem.

INTRODUCTION

Within the covers of this book, there are over 190 species of trees and shrubs that once would have been found extensively across the plains and low hills of South India. Many are still commonly found along rural roadsides or tank bunds, while others can be found in the reserve forests and national parks, such as the tiger reserves of Mudumalai or Bandipur. Heading up to the hill stations of the south, such as Ooty and Kodaikanal, the roads pass through the natural habitat of many of these plants.

Another important place to find these native species is in the sacred groves around temples, particularly those connected to the deities of Ayyanar or Mariamman. It is easy to recognize these shrines found at the outer boundary of the village, as there are large, brightly painted horses standing at the entrance. Traditionally, each village would have designated the strongest amongst them to act as the guardian, and they were given the title of Ayyanarappan. They would dwell in the forest on the village outskirts and ensure that no unwanted person enters the village with an evil intention. The villagers would pay tribute to this warrior, who was free to hunt in the forest. Over time, the necessity of this role was reduced and became more and more symbolic; hence today we find temples and icons. However, the belief remains that Ayyanarappan and the forest protect the people from flood, cyclone and other natural calamities and are also the source of food, herbal medicines and fodder.

View of the hills of Chengalpattu, near Chennai, highlighting the forested areas essential for the protection of wildlife and biodiversity.

*Natural regeneration of **Hildegardia populifolia**, an endangered species, found in the Pakkamalai Hills, near Gingee.*

History of Puthupet Temple
(one of the main temple groves close to Auroville)

Padmasuran, an asura, after performing very strict tapas, received a boon from Lord Shiva. He was granted the power that whoever he touched on the head with his hand would turn into ashes. Being the disreputable character he was, Padmasuran decided to check if the boon worked by attempting to touch the head of Lord Shiva. Lord Shiva fled in fear to the forest and hid himself in an Adhandankai—a large climbing plant (*Capparis zeylanica*).

There he stayed until Lord Vishnu came to the rescue disguised as a beautiful woman who mesmerized the demon. She (Lord Vishnu) imposed a condition on the demon, that if he desired to be with her, he must put water on his head, rub and make himself clean. The demon, while doing so, turned into ashes due to the boon he had received from Lord Shiva.

Later, Lord Shiva married the woman (Lord Vishnu), and the couple gave birth to a child who was named as Ayyanarappan and he was worshipped as the deity of the Pudupet forest.

Aside from patches of forest, individual trees and shrubs are also found around the edges of agricultural lands, and in refuges tucked away in the inaccessible reaches of the hills that are scattered across the plains. In urban areas, they can often be found in city parks and green spaces. Of particular note is the extraordinary Guindy National Park in Chennai, which is predominantly made up of native species. Other urban parks, such as Cubbon Park in Bangalore, have of course been planted with exotic species over the years, but there are also native species to be found amongst the newer arrivals. Other places to find these trees in the cities include green spaces around colleges and government buildings. They may also be found growing in unexpected places, possibly as a result of a population that was there before the city grew up around it, or from a seed dropped by a passing bird.

The climate of the region has the greatest influence on the species composition of the forests, and is dominated by hot and dry summers, two monsoons, and rainfall patterns that vary from 600 to 1350 mm per annum due to the rain shadow effect of the Western Ghats and Sri Lanka. This rain shadow is particularly pronounced in the southern tip of the peninsula, and it is here that low precipitation-adapted species such as *Balanites roxburghii*, *Albizia lathamii* and *Salvadora persica* can be found.

As the foothills of the Western Ghats and central plains receive most of their rain from the southwest monsoon, the forests here tend to have higher concentrations of deciduous species such as *Albizia amara*, *Hardwickia binata* and *Terminalia paniculata*. These deciduous species tend to put out their blooms in February and March so that the seeds are mature and ready for the onset of the southwest monsoon that arrives in the summer. In contrast, the

*The Pakkamalai Hills are the natural habitat of **Drypetes porteri**, an endangered species.*

coastal regions, which have more rain from the northeast monsoon, have a greater concentration of evergreen species such as *Diospyros ebenum*, *Memecylon umbellatum* and *Walsura trifoliata*. In this situation, the flowering is less predictable, as the evergreen species tend to wait until the first spring showers have arrived before they open their buds. The perfume of their flowers, designed to attract pollinating insects or, in some cases, bats, adds a pleasant distraction to the hot summer breeze. As summer progresses, the seeds mature in time for the northeast monsoon that arrives in the autumn. These rains, blowing in from the Bay of Bengal, provide an extended growing season for the freshly germinating seedlings.

This effect of the two monsoons on the species composition of the forests is not a hard and fast rule as nature cannot be so easily boxed, but in general, it is seen that the Tropical Dry Evergreen Forests of the Coromandel Coast transition smoothly into the Tropical Dry Deciduous Forests as one moves further inland, or up into the small hillocks that are dotted across the plains of all the southern states.

THE FUTURE OF THE FOREST

Until a few thousand years ago, the peninsula of South India would have been one contiguous forest stretching from the coastal belt, across the plains, and to the hills of the Western Ghats. Within this vast range there would have been a number of distinct forest types adapted to variations in rainfall, soil type and altitude. Animal and bird populations would have roamed freely throughout the area, adding their own signature to the landscape through grazing and other forms of disturbance. They would have also acted as agents of seed dispersal, ensuring the trees and shrubs were able to spread over the land to find specialized niches within which they could thrive.

*Flower of **Hildegardia populifolia***

Since the arrival of humans, some ten thousand years ago, the landscape has been fundamentally re-designed. Forests are confined to distinct patches, more often than not in areas unsuited to agricultural practices. Additionally, many of these remaining forests have been subjected to degrading practices, particularly during the colonial period, as timber was extracted, and the remaining species cut down and turned into charcoal to fuel the railways and industry. At this time, the deforested areas might have been replanted as monocultural timber or fuelwood plots or left to regenerate on their own after harvesting. In the latter case, the species distribution skewed towards the plants able to coppice from cut stems or those that managed to regenerate in the full sun while protecting themselves from grazing pressure through the presence of thorns.

Today, the majority of people living in these regions have little, or no, reference from which to visualize how the land once was. Nor can they imagine the beneficial effects that the forest would have bestowed upon the environment, in

*A rare encounter of **Albizzia lathamii**, an endangered species, found in a sacred grove near Pandalgudi.*

particular, ameliorating the harsh extremes of the climate in the hot summers, or reducing the impact of the intense monsoonal rains. Large areas are crying out for attention, most noticeably those currently covered with invasive exotic species, such as the Madras thorn (*Prosopis juliflora*), which is a species that can thrive in the current mix of grazing pressure and degraded soil. There are, however, many native trees and shrubs that are uniquely adapted to grow in these degraded lands, and if extensively planted through ecological restoration programmes, these areas would, in time, return to the ecological health once provided by the original forests.

AUROVILLE AND THE AFFORESTATION WORK

The international community of Auroville began in 1968 on an eroded and degraded plateau 12 kilometres north of the city of Puducherry. The inspiration and guidance for the creation of this experiment in Human Unity comes from the teachings and philosophy of Sri Aurobindo and The Mother. The long-term aim is to create a city of around 50,000 people drawn from all the different cultures around the world. Fifty years after its inception there is now a thriving permanent community of over 3,000 people, and a comparable

floating population of students, volunteers, visitors and well-wishers who are involved in the life of the town. However, to get to this point has not been an easy journey, as the initial conditions were extremely challenging. Back in the sixties, the land was eroded and treeless. The fertile land lost to the sea, as the bare sandy soils were highly susceptible to the intense rains of the monsoon. In many places, the topsoil was gone and deep canyons had been carved into the landscape of red laterite subsoil. Leaving the land only fit for wandering herds of goats to graze on the seasonal grasses that still managed to grow in the short post-monsoonal season. In the hot summer months, the area was empty and lifeless.

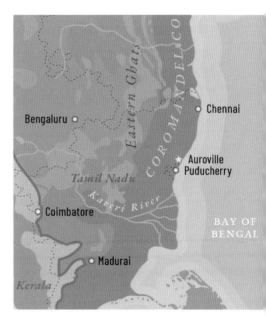

For the early settlers of Auroville, it was clear that the major imperative was to stop the loss of soil to the rains through water harvesting, and to create shelter from the sun and dust storms by planting trees. The seedlings of the initial plantations came from outside nurseries and were of mixed origin. Some were ornamental trees found in commercial nurseries; others were exotic pioneer species promoted by the government nurseries. The plantations were experimental as the conditions were harsh and many of the more ornamental species failed to make it through the summer months. So there was a process of selection; the knowledge of successful species was shared amongst the earlier pioneers, and consequently, in the following years, the trees more adapted to the tough conditions were planted in greater numbers. Most notable amongst these was a tree from North West Queensland in Australia, *Acacia auriculiformis*. This tree ticked all the boxes and more. It managed to survive through the extreme summer temperatures and withstand the hot drying winds that raced across the plateau before the advent of the summer monsoon. It had the ability to fix its own nitrogen, which was extremely advantageous as the eroded soils were poor in nutrients. And it grew quickly, gaining enough height and girth after the first couple of growing seasons to take its growing tips away from the goats and cattle that still roam the plateau and manage to break the fences created to protect these initial plantations. Other species, such as *Acacia holosericea, Cassia siamea, Khaya senegalensis* and some species of Eucalyptus, to name a few, also managed to establish and contribute to the young emerging forests of Auroville.

As the forest started to flourish, the immediate emergency was dealt with, shade was established and a liveable environment created. People's time and energy were no longer solely dedicated to the protection and nurturing of the initial plantations. Interest in what would have been the natural forest cover of the area emerged, and a small group began to explore the local area searching for clues and remnants. It was from this initial curiosity that the presence of the temple groves was discovered, which led to the development of a systematic study of the native vegetation. Species were identified from existing floras; seeds were collected, germination techniques established, and gradually, the tree nurseries of Auroville filled up with an ever-increasing diversity of native species. Fortuitously, these evergreen species of the TDEF are adapted to establish in the shade of mature forest, and so they managed to fit neatly under the emerging canopy of the newly planted forests

Ecological restoration of the Tropical Dry Evergreen Forest in the Auroville Botanical Gardens, where all of the species found in this book now grow.

of Auroville. Once again, a living experiment began, to understand the techniques required to recreate a native, evergreen forest. This work continues today in Auroville, with many rare and threatened species now well established in the forest, many of them seeding and naturally regenerating themselves. And it is these species that you can find in this book, that now make up the forest of Auroville.

The Auroville Botanical Gardens was established in August 2000 to study, conserve and restore the endangered TDEF forests. Initially, the land was devoid of any tree cover, but since then, the 50-acre site has been transformed into an ecologically rich landscape, that serves as an area for research into environmentally

sustainable approaches to land management and plant conservation, as well as a location for environmental and horticultural education.

The gardens are now well established as a centre of environmental education for the schools of the local bioregion and every year there are a number of training courses that pass on the knowledge required for undertaking ecological restoration projects to mature students.

Within the gardens there are a number of distinct areas, such as the conservation forest, which, after the initial plantation with native TDEF species, has been left alone to develop as a sanctuary area. Adjacent to this is the arboretum, which has more of a park-like atmosphere, and is

home to over 250 species of tropical trees, both native and non-native. And then there are the speciality gardens, which house extensive collections of plant types, such as orchids, ferns, cactus, cycads, plumerias, bamboos etc.

The development of the gardens has been a step by step process, with ideas manifesting as and when the funds are available, which depends on the income generated by outside projects the team at the gardens are able to work on. Over the past 15 years, numerous landscaping and restoration projects around India have been undertaken, and over a million native trees have been grown and dispatched to planting projects from the nursery at the garden. In recent years the scale of the projects has increased, with the undertaking of large eco-restoration initiatives at the exhausted mines of Ramco Cements. These projects are still active and expanding; to date, they have covered over 300 acres and in the next 3 to 4 years these areas will more than double. The aspiration of the team at the Auroville Botanical Gardens is to train more young people through the annual Ecological Horticultural Course so that more projects of this scale can be initiated with an ever-increasing circle of participating individuals, companies and institutions.

HOW TO IDENTIFY PLANTS WITH THIS BOOK

The abbreviations are:
(c) Common name
(T) Tamil name
(H) Hindi name
(M) Mother's spiritual name

On the outer edge of each page
is a key with symbols.

This indicates whether the plant
is **Deciduous**, **Brevideciduous**,
or **Evergreen**.

This symbol corresponds to
one of five possible **leaf types**:
Simple, Lobed, Pinnate,
Digitate or Palm.

This symbol corresponds to one of
five possible **leaf arrangements**:
Alternate, Decussate, Opposite,
Spiral or Whorled.

GT is for **Germination Time**.
GR is for **Germination Rate**.

Next to this is a symbol
for the **flower colour**.

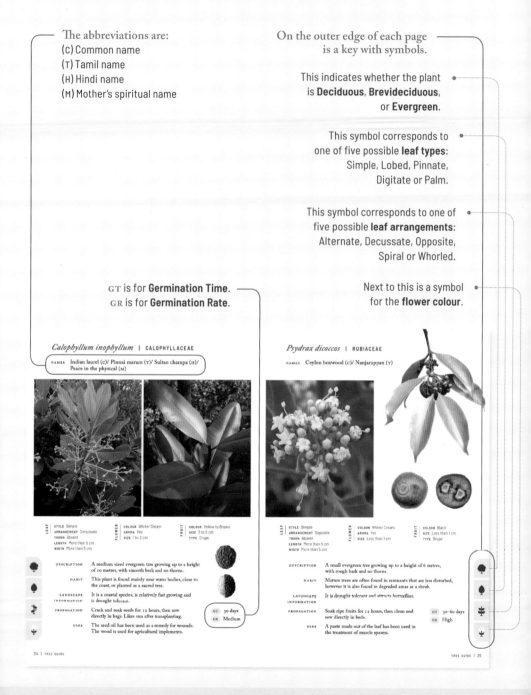

Calophyllum inophyllum | CALOPHYLLACEAE

NAMES Indian laurel (c)/ Pinnai maram (T)/ Sultan champa (H)/
Peace in the physical (M)

LEAF			FLOWER			FRUIT		
STYLE	Simple		COLOUR	White/ Cream		COLOUR	Yellow to Brown	
ARRANGEMENT	Decussate		AROMA	Yes		SIZE	3 to 5 cm	
THORN	Absent		SIZE	1 to 3 cm		TYPE	Drupe	
LENGTH	More than 5 cm							
WIDTH	More than 5 cm							

DESCRIPTION A medium sized evergreen tree growing up to a height
of 10 metres, with smooth bark and no thorns.

HABIT This plant is found mainly near water bodies, close to
the coast, or planted as a sacred tree.

LANDSCAPE INFORMATION It is a coastal species, is relatively fast growing and
is drought tolerant.

PROPAGATION Crack and soak seeds for 12 hours, then sow
directly in bags. Likes sun after transplanting.

USES The seed oil has been used as a remedy for wounds.
The wood is used for agricultural implements.

GT 30 days
GR Medium

Psydrax dicoccos | RUBIACEAE

NAMES Ceylon boxwood (c)/ Nanjaruppan (T)

LEAF			FLOWER			FRUIT		
STYLE	Simple		COLOUR	White/ Cream		COLOUR	Black	
ARRANGEMENT	Opposite		AROMA	Yes		SIZE	Less than 1 cm	
THORN	Absent		SIZE	Less than 1 cm		TYPE	Drupe	
LENGTH	More than 5 cm							

DESCRIPTION A small evergreen tree growing up to a height of 6 metres,
with rough bark and no thorns.

HABIT Mature trees are often found in remnants that are less disturbed,
however it is also found in degraded areas as a shrub.

LANDSCAPE INFORMATION It is drought tolerant and attracts butterflies.

PROPAGATION Soak ripe fruits for 12 hours, then clean and
sow directly in beds.

USES A paste made out of the leaf has been used in
the treatment of muscle spasms.

GT 30–60 days
GR High

If you have difficulty identifying a plant, you can find help on our website:
www.plantekey.com/search

LEAF STYLE

In this book, the species are sorted according to the shape and form of their leaves—using leaf symbols to differentiate between the various possibilities.

 ### Simple

A simple leaf has its blade in one piece. In contrast with a compound leaf, it is not divided up into smaller leaflets.

 ### Lobed

A lobed leaf is a simple leaf that is deeply indented along its margins, but not divided into separate leaflets.

 ### Pinnate

A pinnate leaf is a compound leaf that has a central axis that divides leaflets arranged on either side, which may be opposite or alternate.

 ### Digitate

A digitate leaf is a compound leaf having multiple leaflets that radiate from a central point.

Palm

A palm leaf has a very distinct shape, appearing in either fan or feather shape.

Leaf size and shape can be variable, even on the same tree. In some cases, the juvenile leaf can be very different from those of the mature leaf. In this book, the mature leaf shape and size are described.

Evergreen plants keep their leaves throughout the year.

Deciduous plants seasonally shed all of their leaves, normally during dry and hot periods.

Brevideciduous plants drop all their leaves for a short period (a week or so), before they regrow a completely fresh, new set.

LEAF ARRANGEMENT

The leaf arrangement is another important aid in the identification of the plant. In this book, the species are sorted according to the following five leaf arrangements: alternate, opposite, decussate, spiral, and whorled.

Alternate

Alternate indicates that the leaves are borne along the stem, alternately in a single plane. This is the case for the majority of the plants in this book.

Opposite

Opposite leaves are paired at a node, and found on either side of the stem.

Decussate

Decussate refers to opposite leaves arranged with each succeeding pair at right angles to the pairs below them.

Spiral

Spiral is a type of alternate leaf arrangement, where the leaves on the stem rotate in a spiral, slightly offset from the leaves above, or below them.

Whorled

Whorled is the arrangement of 3 or more leaves that radiate from a single point.

GARLIC PEAR TREE / *Maavilingam*
Crateva adansonii subsp. odora

Calophyllum inophyllum | CALOPHYLLACEAE

NAMES   Indian laurel (C)/ Pinnai maram (T)/ Sultan champa (H)/ Peace in the physical (M)

LEAF
- **STYLE** Simple
- **ARRANGEMENT** Decussate
- **THORN** Absent
- **LENGTH** More than 5 cm
- **WIDTH** More than 5 cm

FLOWER
- **COLOUR** White/ Cream
- **AROMA** Yes
- **SIZE** 1 to 3 cm

FRUIT
- **COLOUR** Yellow to Brown
- **SIZE** 3 to 5 cm
- **TYPE** Drupe

DESCRIPTION	A medium sized evergreen tree growing up to a height of 10 metres, with smooth bark and no thorns.
HABITAT	This plant is found mainly near water bodies, close to the coast, or planted as a sacred tree.
LANDSCAPE INFORMATION	It is a coastal species, is relatively fast growing and is drought tolerant.
PROPAGATION	Crack and soak seeds for 12 hours, then sow directly in bags. Likes sun after transplanting.
USES	The seed oil has been used as a remedy for wounds. The wood is used for agricultural implements.

GT 30 days

GR Medium

Psydrax dicoccos | RUBIACEAE

NAMES   Ceylon boxwood (C)/ Nanjaruppan (T)

LEAF
STYLE Simple
ARRANGEMENT Opposite
THORN Absent
LENGTH More than 5 cm
WIDTH More than 5 cm

FLOWER
COLOUR White/ Cream
AROMA Yes
SIZE Less than 1 cm

FRUIT
COLOUR Black
SIZE Less than 1 cm
TYPE Drupe

DESCRIPTION	A small evergreen tree growing up to a height of 6 metres, with rough bark and no thorns.
HABITAT	Mature trees are often found in remnants that are less disturbed; however, they are also found in degraded areas as shrubs.
LANDSCAPE INFORMATION	It is drought tolerant and attracts butterflies.
PROPAGATION	Soak ripe fruits for 12 hours, then clean and sow directly in beds.
USES	A paste made out of the leaf has been used in the treatment of muscle spasms.

GT   30–60 days
GR   High

Ixora pavetta | RUBIACEAE

NAMES Torch wood tree (c)/ Koran (т)/ Jilpai (н)/
Straightforwardness (м)

LEAF	**STYLE** Simple		**FLOWER**	**COLOUR** White/ Cream		**FRUIT**	**COLOUR** Black
	ARRANGEMENT Opposite			**AROMA** Yes			**SIZE** Less than 1 cm
	THORN Absent			**SIZE** Less than 1 cm			**TYPE** Drupe
	LENGTH More than 5 cm						
	WIDTH More than 5 cm						

DESCRIPTION	An evergreen small tree, with smooth bark and no thorns.
HABITAT	Mature trees are often found in undisturbed remnant forests, however also found in degraded areas as a shrub.
LANDSCAPE INFORMATION	It has fragrant flowers, attracts birds, and is drought tolerant.
PROPAGATION	Clean and soak seeds for 12 hours, then sow in beds or trays. Seedlings require aftercare, and not all develop.
USES	Infusions made from the leaves have been used to treat stomach ache. A decoction of the bark has been used to treat anaemia.

GT 30 days

GR Medium

Pavetta indica | RUBIACEAE

NAMES   Paavattai (T)/ Papat (H)/ Radiating peace in the cells (M)

LEAF
STYLE Simple
ARRANGEMENT Opposite
THORN Absent
LENGTH More than 5 cm
WIDTH More than 5 cm

FLOWER
COLOUR White/ Cream
AROMA Yes
SIZE 1 to 3 cm

FRUIT
COLOUR Black
SIZE Less than 1 cm
TYPE Berry

DESCRIPTION	A brevideciduous shrub, with smooth bark and no thorns.
HABITAT	This shrub can be found in the open, or as a component of the understorey in a mature forest.
LANDSCAPE INFORMATION	It is drought tolerant and attracts butterflies.
PROPAGATION	Clean and soak seeds for 24 hours, then sow in beds or trays.
USES	A decoction made from the whole plant has been known to alleviate body pain. The root is diuretic and purgative.

GT 6 months
GR High

Pleurostylia opposita | CELASTRACEAE

NAMES   Sirupiyari (T)

LEAF
STYLE Simple
ARRANGEMENT Decussate
THORN Absent
LENGTH More than 5 cm
WIDTH 1.5 to 5 cm

FLOWER
COLOUR White
AROMA No
SIZE Less than 1 cm

FRUIT
COLOUR White
SIZE Less than 1 cm
TYPE Drupe

DESCRIPTION	An evergreen small tree, with smooth bark and no thorns.
HABITAT	This shrub can be found in the open, or as a component of the understorey in a mature forest.
LANDSCAPE INFORMATION	It is drought tolerant, has beautiful foliage, and is relatively fast growing.
PROPAGATION	Clean and soak seeds for 6 hours, then sow in beds or trays.
USES	This shrub yields beautiful furniture wood, and it is also used for making combs.

GT   21–30 days
GR   Medium

Tarenna asiatica | RUBIACEAE

NAMES   Tharani (T)/ Bingi papadi (H)/ Humility before the Divine
in the physical nature (M)

LEAF
STYLE Simple
ARRANGEMENT Decussate
THORN Absent
LENGTH More than 5 cm
WIDTH 1.5 to 5 cm

FLOWER
COLOUR White/ Cream
AROMA Yes
SIZE Less than 1 cm

FRUIT
COLOUR Black
SIZE Less than 1 cm
TYPE Berry

DESCRIPTION	An evergreen shrub, with smooth bark and no thorns.
HABITAT	This shrub can be found in the open, or as a component of the understorey in a mature forest.
LANDSCAPE INFORMATION	It is drought tolerant, has beautiful foliage, and is relatively fast growing.
PROPAGATION	Clean and soak seeds for 12 hours, when dry sow in beds. Seeds very small.
USES	The leaves have reportedly been used as a treatment for excessive flatulence.

GT   60–90 days

GR   Medium

Tricalysia sphaerocarpa | RUBIACEAE

NAMES Pachai nazhuvai (T)

LEAF
STYLE Simple
ARRANGEMENT Decussate
THORN Absent
LENGTH More than 5 cm
WIDTH 1.5 to 5 cm

FLOWER
COLOUR White/Cream
AROMA Yes
SIZE Less than 1 cm

FRUIT
COLOUR Green
SIZE 1 to 3 cm
TYPE Berry

DESCRIPTION	A small evergreen tree growing up to a height of 6 metres, with smooth bark and no thorns. Also known as *Discospermum sphaerocarpum*.
HABITAT	Mature specimens are often found in undisturbed forest remnants, however it can also be found in degraded areas in a modified form.
LANDSCAPE INFORMATION	It is drought tolerant, has beautiful foliage, and is relatively fast growing.
PROPAGATION	Soak seeds for 12 hours before sowing.
USES	The wood is used for making combs.

GT 7–10 days

GR High

Cassine glauca | CELASTRACEAE

NAMES Ceylon tea (c)/ Kanneer maram (T)/ Jamrassi (H)

LEAF
STYLE Simple
ARRANGEMENT Opposite
THORN Absent
LENGTH More than 5 cm
WIDTH 1.5 to 5 cm

FLOWER
COLOUR Green
AROMA No
SIZE Less than 1 cm

FRUIT
COLOUR White
SIZE Less than 1 cm
TYPE Drupe

DESCRIPTION	A medium sized evergreen tree growing up to a height of 10 metres, with rough bark and no thorns.
HABITAT	Mature specimens can be found as standalone trees, or in remnants that are less disturbed. It can also be found in hedgerows in a modified form.
LANDSCAPE INFORMATION	It is drought tolerant, has beautiful foliage, and is relatively fast growing.
PROPAGATION	Soak for 12 hours, then clean and sow directly in bags or beds.
USES	The root has been used for snake bites and swelling. The wood is useful in making cabinets, combs and picture frames.

GT 30 days
GR High

Strychnos nux-vomica | LOGANIACEAE

NAMES   Poison nut (c)/ Etti (T)/ Jahar (H)

LEAF	**FLOWER**	**FRUIT**
STYLE Simple	**COLOUR** Green	**COLOUR** Orange
ARRANGEMENT Opposite	**AROMA** Yes	**SIZE** 2 to 5 cm
THORN Absent	**SIZE** Less than 1 cm	**TYPE** Berry
LENGTH More than 5 cm		
WIDTH More than 5 cm		

DESCRIPTION   A medium sized evergreen tree growing up to a height of 10 metres, with smooth bark and no thorns.

HABITAT   Mature specimens are often found as standalone trees or in hedgerows, however also found in degraded areas in a modified form.

LANDSCAPE INFORMATION   It is slow-growing and drought tolerant.

PROPAGATION   Clean seeds and soak for 24 hours, then sow in beds or trays.

GT   30 days

GR   Medium

USES   This plant is used in Ayurvedic and homoeopathic medicine. The seeds, flowers and bark contain poisonous compounds and should be treated with care.

Strychnos potatorum | LOGANIACEAE

NAMES   Clearing nut (c)/ Thetraan kottai (T)/ Khaia (H)

LEAF
STYLE Simple
ARRANGEMENT Opposite
THORN Absent
LENGTH More than 5 cm
WIDTH 1.5 to 5 cm

FLOWER
COLOUR White/Cream
AROMA Yes
SIZE Less than 1 cm

FRUIT
COLOUR Purple/Blue
SIZE 1 to 3 cm
TYPE Berry

DESCRIPTION	A medium sized deciduous tree growing up to a height of 10 metres, with rough bark and no thorns.
HABITAT	This tree enjoys the full sun, it is a component of the deciduous forest type, and is rarely found in mature evergreen stands.
LANDSCAPE INFORMATION	This is a beautiful, slow-growing tree.
PROPAGATION	Clean seeds and soak for 24 hours, then sow in beds or trays.
USES	The seed paste has reported use as a local application for diabetes, for eye diseases and for stimulating body strength. It is also used to clarify drinking water.

GT 30 days
GR Medium

Garcinia spicata | CLUSIACEAE

NAMES   Bitter garcinia (C)/ Kaattuppinnai (T)/ Tavir (H)

LEAF
STYLE Simple
ARRANGEMENT Opposite
THORN Absent
LENGTH More than 5 cm
WIDTH 1.5 to 5 cm

FLOWER
COLOUR Yellow
AROMA Yes
SIZE Less than 1 cm

FRUIT
COLOUR Yellow
SIZE 3 to 5 cm
TYPE Berry

DESCRIPTION   A medium sized evergreen tree growing up to a height of 10 metres, with smooth bark and no thorns.

HABITAT   Mature specimens are found close to the coast in forest remnants that are generally undisturbed.

LANDSCAPE INFORMATION   It is drought tolerant, has evergreen foliage, and is slow-growing. Can be grown by direct sowing of seeds in the shade.

PROPAGATION   Clean and wash seeds, no need to soak them. Sow directly in bags, and keep seedlings in the shade.

GT   21–30 days
GR   High

USES   The seed oil has been used as a treatment for skin diseases. The wood is useful for general construction purposes.

Syzygium cumini | MYRTACEAE

NAMES Indian blackberry (c)/ Naaval (t)/ Jamun (h)/ Mastery (m)

LEAF
STYLE Simple
ARRANGEMENT Opposite
THORN Absent
LENGTH More than 5 cm
WIDTH 1.5 to 5 cm

FLOWER
COLOUR White/Cream
AROMA Yes
SIZE 1 to 3 cm

FRUIT
COLOUR Purple/Blue
SIZE 3 to 5 cm
TYPE Berry

DESCRIPTION	A medium sized tree growing up to a height of 10 metres, brevideciduous, with smooth bark and no thorns.
HABITAT	A common tree found in disturbed areas, as well as a component of mature forest stands.
LANDSCAPE INFORMATION	It is drought tolerant, has beautiful foliage, attracts animals and birds, and is relatively fast growing.
PROPAGATION	Clean and soak seeds for 12 hours, then sow directly in bags.
USES	The fruit is edible for humans and many other animals. The bark has been used for menstrual problems, and the seed powder to treat diabetes.

GT 7–10 days
GR Very High

Holarrhena pubescens | APOCYNACEAE

NAMES   Bitter oleander (C)/ Kirimalligai (T)/ Samoka (H)/ Psychic peace (M)

LEAF
STYLE Simple
ARRANGEMENT Opposite
THORN Absent
LENGTH More than 5 cm
WIDTH 1.5 to 5 cm

FLOWER
COLOUR White/Cream
AROMA Yes
SIZE 1 to 3 cm

FRUIT
COLOUR Brown/Rusty
SIZE More than 5 cm
TYPE Capsule

DESCRIPTION   A small deciduous tree growing up to a height of 6 metres, with smooth bark and no thorns. Also known as *Holarrhena antidysenterica*.

HABITAT   This tree enjoys the full sun. It is a component of the deciduous forest type and is now used in landscaping.

LANDSCAPE INFORMATION   It is a small tree, with beautiful flowers. It is good as a feature in the garden.

PROPAGATION   Clean seeds and soak for a few hours, then sow in trays. Germination is spread out over a number of weeks.

GT   7–10 days
GR   Medium

USES   Called 'Kurchi' in Ayurveda, its seeds, leaves and bark are used to treat dysentery and diarrhoea.

Wrightia arborea | APOCYNACEAE

NAMES Woolly dyeing rosebay (c)/ Karupaalai (т)/ Pailari (н)

LEAF
STYLE Simple
ARRANGEMENT Opposite
THORN Absent
LENGTH More than 5 cm
WIDTH 1.5 to 5 cm

FLOWER
COLOUR White/Cream
AROMA No
SIZE 1 to 3 cm

FRUIT
COLOUR Brown/Rusty
SIZE More than 5 cm
TYPE Seedpod

DESCRIPTION	A small deciduous tree growing up to a height of 6 metres, with smooth bark and no thorns.
HABITAT	This tree enjoys the full sun. It is a component of the deciduous forest type.
LANDSCAPE INFORMATION	This is a small tree, with beautiful flowers. It is good as a feature in the garden.
PROPAGATION	Clean seeds and soak for a few hours, then sow in trays. Germination is spread out over a number of weeks.
USES	A blue dye is obtained from the seeds, roots and leaves. The wood is valuable timber.

GT 7–10 days
GR Medium

Wrightia tinctoria | APOCYNACEAE

NAMES   Pala indigo (c)/ Vetpaalai (T)/ Doodhi (H)/ Religious thought (M)

LEAF
STYLE Simple
ARRANGEMENT Opposite
THORN Absent
LENGTH More than 5 cm
WIDTH 1.5 to 5 cm

FLOWER
COLOUR White/Cream
AROMA Yes
SIZE 1 to 3 cm

FRUIT
COLOUR Brown/Rusty
SIZE More than 5 cm
TYPE Seedpod

DESCRIPTION   A medium sized deciduous tree growing up to a height of 10 metres, with rough bark and no thorns.

HABITAT   This tree enjoys the full sun. It is often found in rocky areas as a component of the deciduous forest type, and it is rarely found in mature evergreen stands.

LANDSCAPE INFORMATION   This tree is good as a feature in the garden.

PROPAGATION   Clean seeds and soak for a few hours, then sow in beds or trays. Germination is spread out over a number of weeks.

GT   7–10 days
GR   Medium

USES   The leaves have been used to treat dog bites. The wood is used for making toys and temple carts.

Lagerstroemia parviflora | LYTHRACEAE

NAMES   Small flowered crape myrtle (C)/ Chenangi (T)/ Lendia (H)

LEAF
STYLE Simple
ARRANGEMENT Opposite
THORN Absent
LENGTH 1.5 to 5 cm
WIDTH 1.5 to 5 cm

FLOWER
COLOUR White/Cream
AROMA No
SIZE 1 to 3 cm

FRUIT
COLOUR Brown/Rusty
SIZE 1 to 3 cm
TYPE Capsule

DESCRIPTION A medium sized deciduous tree growing up to a height of 10 metres, with rough bark and no thorns.

HABITAT This tree is found on the hillocks. It requires a well drained soil, and a good amount of light to flourish.

LANDSCAPE INFORMATION With its beautiful foliage and delicate flowers, this tree is very attractive.

PROPAGATION Soak seeds overnight, then sow in trays.

USES It is a valuable tree for its timber as the wood is very hard and durable. The bark contains tannins to make a black dye, and its fibres make rough ropes.

GT 2 weeks
GR Medium

Terminalia arjuna | COMBRETACEAE

NAMES   Arjuna (c)/ Marudha maram (t)/ Kahua (h)

LEAF		FLOWER		FRUIT	
STYLE	Simple	COLOUR	Yellow	COLOUR	Brown/Rusty
ARRANGEMENT	Opposite	AROMA	Yes	SIZE	More than 5 cm
THORN	Absent	SIZE	Less than 1 cm	TYPE	Drupe
LENGTH	More than 5 cm				
WIDTH	1.5 to 5 cm				

DESCRIPTION	A large, spreading deciduous tree growing over 10 metres in height, with smooth bark and no thorns.
HABITAT	This tree is naturally found along rivers, although now extensively planted around tanks and in afforestation projects.
LANDSCAPE INFORMATION	This tree is slow-growing, has beautiful bark, and is drought tolerant.
PROPAGATION	Soak seeds for a few days. When fruit opens, extract seeds, then sow in beds.
USES	The bark is reportedly used for the treatment of cardiovascular ailments, while the bark ash may help in treating scorpion stings.

GT   21–30 days

GR   Medium

Terminalia bellirica | COMBRETACEAE

NAMES   Belliric myrobalan (C)/ Thandrikkai (T)/ Bahera (H)

LEAF
STYLE Simple
ARRANGEMENT Alternate
THORN Absent
LENGTH More than 5 cm
WIDTH More than 5 cm

FLOWER
COLOUR White/Cream
AROMA Yes
SIZE Less than 1 cm

FRUIT
COLOUR Brown/Rusty
SIZE 3 to 5 cm
TYPE Drupe

DESCRIPTION	A medium sized deciduous tree growing up to a height of 10 metres, with smooth bark and no thorns.
HABITAT	This plant enjoys the full sun, is a component of the deciduous forest type, and is rarely found in mature evergreen stands. It is often planted on tank bunds.
LANDSCAPE INFORMATION	It is drought tolerant, has beautiful foliage, and is relatively fast growing.
PROPAGATION	Clean and soak seeds for 12 hours, then sow straight into bags.
USES	Known as 'Bibhitaki' in Ayurveda, it is a component of the triphala medicine. The wood is valued as construction material.

GT 30 days
GR High

Terminalia chebula | COMBRETACEAE

NAMES Black myrobalam (C)/ Kaukkaai (T)/ Harra (H)

LEAF
STYLE Simple
ARRANGEMENT Opposite
THORN Absent
LENGTH More than 5 cm
WIDTH 1.5 to 5 cm

FLOWER
COLOUR Cream
AROMA Yes
SIZE Less than 1 cm

FRUIT
COLOUR Yellow
SIZE More than 5 cm
TYPE Drupe

DESCRIPTION
A medium, sized deciduous tree growing up to a height of 10 metres, with rough bark and no thorns.

HABITAT
This tree enjoys the full sun. It is found as a standalone tree in agricultural land, as a component of the deciduous forest type, and rarely found in mature evergreen stands.

LANDSCAPE INFORMATION
It can be used for variety in the landscape.

PROPAGATION
Clean and soak seeds for 12 hours, then sow directly in bags.

USES
A decoction made from the fruit has been used as a remedy for constipation. It is regarded as the best natural tanning agent.

GT 30 days
GR High

Terminalia paniculata | COMBRETACEAE

NAMES Kindal tree (c)/ Pillai marudhu (T)/ Asvakarnah (H)

LEAF
STYLE Simple
ARRANGEMENT Opposite
THORN Absent
LENGTH More than 5 cm
WIDTH More than 5 cm

FLOWER
COLOUR White/Cream
AROMA Yes
SIZE Less than 1 cm

FRUIT
COLOUR Brown/Rusty
SIZE Less than 1 cm
TYPE Drupe

DESCRIPTION	A large, spreading deciduous tree growing over 10 metres in height, with rough bark and no thorns.
HABITAT	This tree enjoys the full sun. It is found as a standalone tree in the hills, as a component of the deciduous forest type, and is rarely found in mature evergreen stands.
LANDSCAPE INFORMATION	This is a beautiful, slow-growing tree.
PROPAGATION	A large quantity of seeds need to be sown and kept moist for 6 months or more.
USES	The flowers have been used as a remedy for cholera. The wood is used for general construction purposes.

GT Unknown
GR Low

IRONWOOD / *Anjan*
Memecylon umbellatum

Haldina cordifolia | RUBIACEAE

NAMES Yellow teak (c)/ Manja kadambu (T)/ Karam (H)

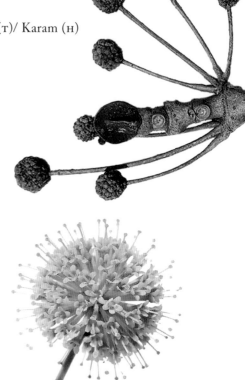

LEAF
STYLE Simple
ARRANGEMENT Opposite
THORN Absent
LENGTH More than 5 cm
WIDTH More than 5 cm

FLOWER
COLOUR Yellow/Orange
AROMA No
SIZE 1 to 3 cm

FRUIT
COLOUR Brown/Rusty
SIZE 1 to 3 cm
TYPE Capsule

DESCRIPTION
A medium sized deciduous tree growing up to a height of 10 metres, with rough bark and no thorns. Also known as *Adina cordifolia*.

HABITAT
This tree enjoys the full sun. It is a component of the deciduous forest type, but occasionally it can be found in mature evergreen stands.

LANDSCAPE INFORMATION
This tree has beautiful foliage and form.

PROPAGATION
Clean seeds and spread in trays. Keep soil moist and transplant only after first leaves appear. Spray copper sulphate against fungus.

GT 10–14 days
GR Medium to Low

USES
In Ayurveda, it has been used to treat skin diseases and indigestion.

Mitragyna parvifolia | RUBIACEAE

NAMES Kaim (c)/ Neerkkadambai (T)/ Guri (H)

LEAF
STYLE Simple
ARRANGEMENT Opposite
THORN Absent
LENGTH More than 5 cm
WIDTH More than 5 cm

FLOWER
COLOUR White/Cream
AROMA Yes
SIZE 1 to 3 cm

FRUIT
COLOUR Brown/Rusty
SIZE Less than 1 cm
TYPE Capsule

DESCRIPTION A medium sized deciduous tree growing up to a height of 10 metres, with smooth bark and no thorns.

HABITAT This plant is a component of riverine vegetation, and is found mainly near ponds or seasonal streams.

LANDSCAPE INFORMATION It is drought tolerant, has beautiful foliage, and is relatively fast growing.

PROPAGATION Clean seeds and spread in trays, keeping them always moist. Transplant only after a few leaves appear. Spray copper sulphate against fungus. Requires half sun.

GT 10–14 days
GR Medium to Low

USES This tree provides valuable timber for planks and rafters.

Carissa spinarum | APOCYNACEAE

NAMES   Currant bush (c)/ Kalakai (T)/
Kanuvan (H)

LEAF		FLOWER		FRUIT	
STYLE	Simple	COLOUR	White/Cream	COLOUR	Black
ARRANGEMENT	Opposite	AROMA	Yes	SIZE	Less than 1 cm
THORN	Straight	SIZE	1 to 3 cm	TYPE	Berry
LENGTH	3 to 5 cm				
WIDTH	1.5 to 5 cm				

DESCRIPTION   A deciduous straggler, with smooth bark and thorns.

HABITAT   This shrub is found either in mature stands reaching up into the canopy, or in more disturbed areas straggling over other plants.

LANDSCAPE INFORMATION   It is drought tolerant, has beautiful foliage, and is relatively fast growing.

PROPAGATION   Clean seeds and soak for 12 hours, then sow in trays.

GT   1 month

GR   High

USES   The fruits are edible, and the roots mixed with coconut milk have been used to treat mouth ulcers.

Clerodendrum inerme | LAMIACEAE

NAMES   Seaside clerodendron (c)/ Peechangan (T)/
Sankuppi (H)/ Perfect planning of work (M)

LEAF
STYLE Simple
ARRANGEMENT Opposite
THORN Absent
LENGTH 1 to 3 cm
WIDTH 1.5 to 5 cm

FLOWER
COLOUR White/Cream
AROMA Yes
SIZE 1 to 3 cm

FRUIT
COLOUR Brown/Rusty
SIZE 1 to 3 cm
TYPE Capsule

DESCRIPTION	A deciduous shrub, with smooth bark and no thorns. Also known as *Volkameria inermis*.
HABITAT	A coastal species of disturbed areas, it grows in full sun, disappearing if the canopy closes. Generally, it is a shrub but will grow as a straggler if conditions allow.
LANDSCAPE INFORMATION	It is drought tolerant and attracts butterflies.
PROPAGATION	Clean seeds and soak for 12 hours, then sow in trays or beds. Can propagate from cuttings.
USES	This plant is used in Ayurveda for the treatment of rheumatism and skin diseases.

GT 30–60 days
GR Medium

Clerodendrum phlomidis | LAMIACEAE

NAMES   Sage glory bower (c)/ Thazhudali (T)/ Arni (H)

LEAF
STYLE Simple
ARRANGEMENT Opposite
THORN Absent
LENGTH 1.5 to 5 cm
WIDTH 1.5 to 5 cm

FLOWER
COLOUR White/Cream
AROMA Yes
SIZE 1 to 3 cm

FRUIT
COLOUR Black
SIZE 1 to 3 cm
TYPE Drupe

DESCRIPTION	A deciduous shrub, with smooth bark and no thorns.
HABITAT	This shrub is found mainly in disturbed areas. It grows in full sun, disappearing if the canopy closes.
LANDSCAPE INFORMATION	This shrub is a good component in ecological landscaping. It is a highly medicinal plant.
PROPAGATION	Soak seeds overnight, then sow in beds. Can propagate from cuttings.
USES	Known as 'Agnimatha' in Ayurveda, this plant has many medicinal uses, including relieving body pain and to support bone development.

GT   2 weeks
GR   Medium

Premna corymbosa | LAMIACEAE

NAMES   Munnai (T)

LEAF
STYLE Simple
ARRANGEMENT Opposite
THORN Absent
LENGTH More than 5 cm
WIDTH 1.5 to 5 cm

FLOWER
COLOUR White/Cream
AROMA Yes
SIZE Less than 1 cm

FRUIT
COLOUR Purple/Blue
SIZE Less than 1 cm
TYPE Drupe

DESCRIPTION   A deciduous straggler, with smooth bark and no thorns.

HABITAT   A plant found on the edge of mature stands or in disturbed areas. It can either grow up into the canopy as a straggler, or it can stand alone as a shrub.

LANDSCAPE INFORMATION   It is a good component in ecological landscaping.

PROPAGATION   Clean and soak seeds for 12 hours, then sow in beds or trays. Can propagate from cuttings.

GT   Up to 6 months
GR   Low

USES   The leaf juice has been applied externally for dropsy. The roots have been used as a laxative, and for the treatment of stomach ache.

Premna serratifolia | LAMIACEAE

NAMES Headache tree (c)/ Pasu munnai (t)/ Ageta (h)

LEAF
STYLE Simple
ARRANGEMENT Opposite
THORN Absent
LENGTH More than 5 cm
WIDTH 1.5 to 5 cm

FLOWER
COLOUR White/Cream
AROMA Yes
SIZE Less than 1 cm

FRUIT
COLOUR Black
SIZE Less than 1 cm
TYPE Drupe

DESCRIPTION	A deciduous shrub, with smooth bark and no thorns.
HABITAT	This is a coastal species found in the open, or as a component of the understorey in a mature forest. It will act as a straggler if conditions allow.
LANDSCAPE INFORMATION	It attracts butterflies, is drought tolerant, and can be used as a border plant.
PROPAGATION	Clean and soak seeds for 12 hours, then sow in beds or trays. Can propagate from cuttings.
USES	This plant has traditionally been used for the treatment of rheumatism, neuralgia and headaches.

GT 1 month
GR High

Premna tomentosa | **LAMIACEAE**

NAMES Dusky fire-brand teak (C)/ Erumai munnai (T)/ Bakar (H)

LEAF		FLOWER		FRUIT	
STYLE Simple		**COLOUR** White/Cream		**COLOUR** Red	
ARRANGEMENT Opposite		**AROMA** Yes		**SIZE** Less than 1 cm	
THORN Absent		**SIZE** Less than 1 cm		**TYPE** Drupe	
LENGTH More than 5 cm					
WIDTH 1.5 to 5 cm					

DESCRIPTION A deciduous shrub, with smooth bark and no thorns.

HABITAT This shrub enjoys the full sun. It is generally found on hillocks, and is a component of the deciduous forest type.

LANDSCAPE INFORMATION It attracts bees, is slow-growing, and drought tolerant.

PROPAGATION Clean and soak seeds for 12 hours, then sow in beds or trays.

GT Up to 6 months

GR Low

USES Milky sap extracted from the bark has been applied as a treatment for boils, and the leaves are reported to be diuretic.

Benkara malabarica | RUBIACEAE

NAMES Sirukarai (T)

LEAF
STYLE Simple
ARRANGEMENT Opposite
THORN Straight
LENGTH More than 5 cm
WIDTH 1.5 to 5 cm

FLOWER
COLOUR White/Cream
AROMA Yes
SIZE Less than 1 cm

FRUIT
COLOUR Black
SIZE Less than 1 cm
TYPE Berry

DESCRIPTION	A deciduous shrub, with smooth bark and thorns.
HABITAT	A shrub found mainly in disturbed areas, it grows in full sun, disappearing if the canopy closes.
LANDSCAPE INFORMATION	It can be used as a live fence, it attracts butterflies, birds eat the fruit, and it is drought tolerant.
PROPAGATION	Clean and soak seeds for 12 hours, then sow in beds or trays. Seedling aftercare required after transplanting.
USES	This plant has been used in treating diarrhoea, dysentery, abdominal pain, and throat infections.

GT 60–90 days
GR Low

Catunaregam spinosa | RUBIACEAE

NAMES Emetic nut (c)/ Madhukkarai (t)/ Mainhar (h)

LEAF	STYLE Simple	**FLOWER**	COLOUR White/Cream	**FRUIT**	COLOUR Yellow
	ARRANGEMENT Opposite		AROMA Yes		SIZE 1 to 3 cm
	THORN Straight		SIZE 1 to 3 cm		TYPE Berry
	LENGTH 1 to 3 cm				
	WIDTH 0.5 to 1.5 cm				

DESCRIPTION A deciduous shrub, with smooth bark and thorns.

HABITAT This shrub is found mainly in disturbed areas. It grows in the full sun, and disappears if the canopy closes.

LANDSCAPE INFORMATION It is good as a live fence.

PROPAGATION Clean seeds and soak for 12 hours, then sow in trays.

USES The fruits have been used as a fish poison, and the thorns have been used for ear piercing.

GT 21–30 days

GR Medium

Gardenia latifolia | RUBIACEAE

NAMES Boxwood gardenia (C)/
Kaattu marikkalam (T)/ Papda (H)

LEAF
STYLE Simple
ARRANGEMENT Opposite
THORN Absent
LENGTH More than 5 cm
WIDTH More than 5 cm

FLOWER
COLOUR White/Cream
AROMA Yes
SIZE More than 5 cm

FRUIT
COLOUR Brown/Rusty
SIZE 3 to 5 cm
TYPE Berry

DESCRIPTION	A small deciduous tree growing up to a height of 6 metres, with smooth bark and no thorns.
HABITAT	This tree enjoys the full sun. It is often found on hillocks, and is a component of the deciduous forest type. It is rarely found in mature evergreen stands.
LANDSCAPE INFORMATION	It has beautiful flowers, and can be used as a garden feature as it has a lovely form.
PROPAGATION	Clean and soak seeds for 12 hours, then sow in beds or trays. Spray copper sulphate against fungus.
USES	The timber is used for making combs and turnery articles. The fruit, seed and root are used to treat fever.

GT 30 days
GR Medium

Gardenia resinifera | RUBIACEAE

NAMES Brilliant gardenia (c)/ Kambali pisin (t)/ Deekamali (h)

LEAF
STYLE Simple
ARRANGEMENT Opposite
THORN Absent
LENGTH More than 5 cm
WIDTH More than 5 cm

FLOWER
COLOUR White/Cream
AROMA Yes
SIZE More than 5 cm

FRUIT
COLOUR Brown/Rusty
SIZE 3 to 5 cm
TYPE Berry

DESCRIPTION A deciduous shrub, with smooth bark and no thorns.

HABITAT This shrub enjoys the full sun. It is found on hillocks, and is a component of the deciduous forest type. It is rarely found in mature evergreen stands.

LANDSCAPE INFORMATION It is drought tolerant, has beautiful foliage, and is relatively fast growing.

PROPAGATION Clean and soak seeds for 12 hours, then sow in beds or trays. Spray copper sulphate against fungus.

GT 30 days
GR Medium

USES The resin has been used for relieving toothache and fever. The wood is used in turnery and for making combs.

Psilanthus wightianus | RUBIACEAE

NAMES Wild coffee (c)/ Mutti (t)

LEAF		**FLOWER**		**FRUIT**	
STYLE Simple		**COLOUR** White/Cream		**COLOUR** Purple/Blue	
ARRANGEMENT Opposite		**AROMA** Yes		**SIZE** 1 to 3 cm	
THORN Absent		**SIZE** 1 to 3 cm		**TYPE** Berry	
LENGTH 3 to 5 cm					
WIDTH 1.5 to 5 cm					

DESCRIPTION	A deciduous shrub, with smooth bark and no thorns. Also known as *Coffea wightiana*.
HABITAT	This shrub can be found in the open, or as a component of the understorey in a disturbed forest.
LANDSCAPE INFORMATION	It is drought tolerant, and attracts butterflies.
PROPAGATION	Clean and soak seeds for 12 hours, then sow in beds or trays.
USES	The fruits can be used as a substitute for coffee.

GT 21–30 days

GR High

Azima tetracantha | SALVADORACEAE

NAMES Needle bush (c)/ Sangan (T)/ Kantagur kamai (H)

LEAF
STYLE Simple
ARRANGEMENT Opposite
THORN Absent
LENGTH More than 5 cm
WIDTH More than 5 cm

FLOWER
COLOUR White/Cream
AROMA Yes
SIZE More than 5 cm

FRUIT
COLOUR Brown/Rusty
SIZE 3 to 5 cm
TYPE Berry

DESCRIPTION A deciduous shrub, with smooth bark and thorns.

HABITAT This shrub is found mainly in disturbed coastal areas behind mangroves. It grows in full sun, and disappears if the canopy closes.

LANDSCAPE INFORMATION It is an effective hedge plant, is drought tolerant, and is slow-growing.

PROPAGATION Clean and soak seeds for 12 hours, then sow in beds.

USES A decoction made from the leaves has been used as a remedy for gastric conditions and for colds, the roots a remedy for snake bites, and the berry juice for earache.

GT 30–60 days
GR Medium

Santalum album | SANTALACEAE

NAMES Sandalwood (c)/ Sandhanam (T)/ Chandan (H)

LEAF
STYLE Simple
ARRANGEMENT Opposite
THORN Absent
LENGTH 3 to 5 cm
WIDTH 1.5 to 5 cm

FLOWER
COLOUR White/Cream
AROMA Yes
SIZE 1 to 3 cm

FRUIT
COLOUR Purple/Blue
SIZE 1 to 3 cm
TYPE Berry

DESCRIPTION
A small deciduous tree growing up to a height of 6 metres, with smooth bark and no thorns.

HABITAT
This tree is occasionally found in forest areas, however it is more usually found as a small sapling by the side of the road, on tank bunds, or in agricultural boundaries.

LANDSCAPE INFORMATION
This is a beautiful, slow-growing tree. Listed as vulnerable on the IUCN Red List.

PROPAGATION
Clean and soak seeds for 12 hours, then sow in beds or trays. Needs host plant to establish after transplanting.

GT 10–14 days
GR High

USES
Fragrant wood. A wood paste can treat headaches and skin diseases.

Stenosiphonium russellianum | ACANTHACEAE

NAMES   Heart-leaf coneflower (C)/ Kattu kurinji (T)

LEAF		FLOWER		FRUIT	
STYLE Simple		**COLOUR** Blue		**COLOUR** Brown/Rusty	
ARRANGEMENT Opposite		**AROMA** No		**SIZE** Less than 1 cm	
THORN Absent		**SIZE** 1 to 3 cm		**TYPE** Capsule	
LENGTH More than 5 cm					
WIDTH 1.5 to 5 cm					

DESCRIPTION | A deciduous shrub, with smooth bark and no thorns.

HABITAT | This shrub is normally found in the understorey of the forest, and only if the canopy has been recently removed will it be found in the open sun.

LANDSCAPE INFORMATION | It attracts butterflies, is drought tolerant, and can be used as a border plant with occasional trimming.

PROPAGATION | Clean and soak seeds for 12 hours, then sow in beds or trays. Can propagate from cuttings.

USES | This plant has been traditionally used as a blood purifier.

GT   1–2 months

GR   Medium

Hymenodictyon orixense | RUBIACEAE

NAMES   Bridal couch tree (c)/ Kothamaram (T)/ Bhormal (H)

LEAF
STYLE Simple
ARRANGEMENT Opposite
THORN Absent
LENGTH More than 5 cm
WIDTH More than 5 cm

FLOWER
COLOUR Green
AROMA No
SIZE Less than 1 cm

FRUIT
COLOUR Brown/Rusty
SIZE 2 to 3 cm
TYPE Capsule

DESCRIPTION	A medium sized deciduous tree growing up to a height of 10 metres, with rough bark and no thorns.
HABITAT	This tree enjoys the full sun. It is a component of the deciduous forest type, and rarely found in mature evergreen stands.
LANDSCAPE INFORMATION	It is drought tolerant, has beautiful foliage, and is relatively fast growing.
PROPAGATION	Clean and soak seeds for 12 hours, then sow in beds or trays.
USES	The bark has been used as an astringent. The wood is a valuable timber, and the leaves are used as cattle fodder.

GT   30 days
GR   Medium

Anogeissus latifolia | COMBRETACEAE

NAMES   Axle wood tree (c)/ Vekkaali (T)/ Dhavda (H)

LEAF
STYLE Simple
ARRANGEMENT Alternate
THORN Absent
LENGTH More than 5 cm
WIDTH 1.5 to 5 cm

FLOWER
COLOUR Yellow
AROMA No
SIZE Less than 1 cm

FRUIT
COLOUR Brown/Rusty
SIZE Less than 1 cm
TYPE Nut

DESCRIPTION	A tall deciduous tree growing over 10 metres in height, with smooth bark and no thorns.
HABITAT	This tree enjoys the full sun. It is a component of the deciduous forest type, and is rarely found in mature evergreen stands.
LANDSCAPE INFORMATION	This is a beautiful, slow-growing tree.
PROPAGATION	Use large numbers of seeds, kept moist in shady area.
USES	This plant has been used for snakebites and scorpion stings. The wood makes a good fuel and fine charcoal, and the timber is strong and durable.

GT   Unknown
GR   Low

Gmelina asiatica | LAMIACEAE

NAMES   Asian bushbeech (C)/ Nilakkumala (T)/ Badhara (H)

LEAF
STYLE Simple
ARRANGEMENT Opposite
THORN Straight
LENGTH 1 to 3 cm
WIDTH 1.5 to 5 cm

FLOWER
COLOUR Yellow
AROMA Yes
SIZE 1 to 3 cm

FRUIT
COLOUR Yellow
SIZE 1 to 3 cm
TYPE Drupe

DESCRIPTION   A deciduous shrub, with smooth bark and thorns.

HABITAT   A plant found mainly in disturbed areas, it grows in full sun, disappearing if the canopy closes.

LANDSCAPE INFORMATION   It is drought tolerant, has beautiful foliage, and is relatively fast growing.

PROPAGATION   Crack and soak seeds for 12 hours, then sow directly in bags or beds. Attacked by squirrels in beds.

USES   Fruit paste applied to the scalp is reported to clear dandruff.

GT   30 days
GR   Medium

Canthium coromandelicum | RUBIACEAE

NAMES   Coromandel boxwood (C)/ Mullukkarai (T)/ Nagabala (H)

LEAF
STYLE Simple
ARRANGEMENT Alternate
THORN Absent
LENGTH More than 5 cm
WIDTH 1.5 to 5 cm

FLOWER
COLOUR Yellow
AROMA No
SIZE Less than 1 cm

FRUIT
COLOUR Brown/Rusty
SIZE Less than 1 cm
TYPE Nut

DESCRIPTION A deciduous shrub, with smooth bark and thorns.

HABITAT A shrub found mainly in disturbed areas. It grows in the full sun, although it is occasionally found as a small tree in mature forest stands.

LANDSCAPE INFORMATION It is a good choice for a live fence.

PROPAGATION Clean seeds and soak for 12 hours, then sow in trays.

GT   1 month
GR   High

USES The plant has been used as a treatment for dysentery, high blood pressure, and to purify the circulatory system.

Chionanthus zeylanicus | OLEACEAE

NAMES   Fringe tree (c)/ Kattimuruchan (T)

LEAF
STYLE Simple
ARRANGEMENT Opposite
THORN Absent
LENGTH More than 5 cm
WIDTH 1.5 to 5 cm

FLOWER
COLOUR White/Cream
AROMA Yes
SIZE Less than 1 cm

FRUIT
COLOUR Purple/Blue
SIZE 1 to 3 cm
TYPE Drupe

DESCRIPTION	A small evergreen tree growing up to a height of 6 metres, with smooth bark and no thorns.
HABITAT	Mature specimens are often found in undisturbed forest remnants, however it can also be found in degraded areas in a modified form.
LANDSCAPE INFORMATION	It is drought tolerant, has evergreen foliage, and is slow-growing.
PROPAGATION	Clean and crack seeds, then sow deep in beds (2 cm). Take care when transplanting as root may be very deep.
USES	Bark extracts have been shown to have antioxidant activity.

GT   1–2 years
GR   Medium

Morinda coreia | RUBIACEAE

NAMES   Forest noni (c)/ Nuna (T)/ Achi (H)

LEAF		FLOWER		FRUIT	
STYLE Simple		**COLOUR** White/Cream		**COLOUR** Black	
ARRANGEMENT Decussate		**AROMA** Yes		**SIZE** 1 to 3 cm	
THORN Absent		**SIZE** 1 to 3 cm		**TYPE** Berry	
LENGTH More than 5 cm					
WIDTH 1.5 to 5 cm					

DESCRIPTION	A small evergreen tree growing up to a height of 6 metres, with rough bark and no thorns.
HABITAT	This plant is occasionally found in forest areas, however it is more usually found by the side of the road, on tank bunds, or in agricultural boundaries.
LANDSCAPE INFORMATION	It is fast growing, relatively short lived, and is good for creating an early canopy.
PROPAGATION	Clean and soak seeds for 12 hours, then sow in beds or trays.
USES	A decoction made from the leaves has been used for stomach problems. The wood is valuable for agricultural implements, and carts.

GT   4–6 months

GR   Medium

Buchanania axillaris | ANACARDIACEAE

NAMES Cuddapah almond (c)/ Kolamaavu (T)/ Char (H)

LEAF		FLOWER		FRUIT	
STYLE	Simple	**COLOUR**	White/Cream	**COLOUR**	Violet
ARRANGEMENT	Alternate	**AROMA**	Yes	**SIZE**	Less than 1 cm
THORN	Absent	**SIZE**	Less than 1 cm	**TYPE**	Drupe
LENGTH	More than 5 cm				
WIDTH	1.5 to 5 cm				

DESCRIPTION — A medium sized evergreen tree growing up to a height of 10 metres, with rough bark and no thorns.

HABITAT — This tree enjoys the full sun, and it is found in remnant forest areas.

LANDSCAPE INFORMATION — This is a beautiful, slow-growing tree.

PROPAGATION — Clean seeds and soak for 12 hours, then sow 2 seeds directly per bag. High mortality rate post germination.

GT 30 days

GR Medium

USES — The seeds have been used as a general tonic, and the powdered bark mixed with honey has been used for dysentery.

Celtis philippensis | CANNABACEAE

NAMES   Vellai thovarai (T)

LEAF	**STYLE** Simple	**FLOWER**	**COLOUR** White/Cream	**FRUIT**	**COLOUR** Orange
	ARRANGEMENT Alternate		**AROMA** No		**SIZE** Less than 1 cm
	THORN Absent		**SIZE** 1 to 3 cm		**TYPE** Drupe
	LENGTH More than 5 cm				
	WIDTH 1.5 to 5 cm				

DESCRIPTION   A small-sized evergreen tree growing up to a height of 6 metres, with smooth bark and no thorns.

HABITAT   A component of mature evergreen stands, this tree is found in the Western Ghats and the lower reaches of the Eastern Ghats.

LANDSCAPE INFORMATION   This is a beautiful, slow-growing tree.

PROPAGATION   Clean seeds and soak for 12 hours, then sow in trays or beds. Seedling aftercare required.

GT 30 days
GR Medium

USES   The seed oil of this tree is edible, and the roots are a reported remedy for diarrhoea. The wood is used for tools and furniture, and the bark can be made into rope and paper.

Diospyros affinis | EBENACEAE

NAMES Chinnathuvarai (T)

LEAF
STYLE Simple
ARRANGEMENT Alternate
THORN Absent
LENGTH More than 5 cm
WIDTH 1.5 to 5 cm

FLOWER
COLOUR White/Cream
AROMA Yes
SIZE 1 to 3 cm

FRUIT
COLOUR Yellow
SIZE 1 to 3 cm
TYPE Berry

DESCRIPTION	A medium sized evergreen tree growing up to a height of 10 metres, with rough bark and no thorns.
HABITAT	Mature specimens are generally found on hillocks rather than on the plains. It is found in undisturbed forest remnants, however it can also be found in degraded areas in a modified form.
LANDSCAPE INFORMATION	It is drought tolerant, has evergreen foliage, and is slow-growing.
PROPAGATION	Clean and soak seeds for 12 hours, then sow directly in bags or beds.
USES	The wood is used for making agricultural implements, carts and furniture.

GT 10–14 days
GR High

Diospyros chloroxylon | EBENACEAE

NAMES   Green ebony persimmon (c)/ Karu vakkanai (T)/ Kinnu (H)

LEAF
STYLE Simple
ARRANGEMENT Alternate
THORN Absent
LENGTH 1 to 3 cm
WIDTH 1.5 to 5 cm

FLOWER
COLOUR White/Cream
AROMA Yes
SIZE Less than 1 cm

FRUIT
COLOUR Green
SIZE 1 to 3 cm
TYPE Berry

DESCRIPTION   A small deciduous tree growing up to a height of 6 metres, with rough bark and thorns found on young growth.

HABITAT   This plant enjoys the full sun. It is found on hillocks, or on tank bunds.

LANDSCAPE INFORMATION   It is a good component in ecological landscaping.

PROPAGATION   Clean and soak seeds for 12 hours, then sow in beds with light soil covering. Sprinkle with wood ash to stop caterpillars.

GT   10–14 days
GR   Low

USES   The fruits are edible, and a paste made out of the leaves has been used as a treatment for burns.

Diospyros ebenum | EBENACEAE

NAMES   Ebony (c)/ Karungaali (T)/ Abnus (H)

LEAF
STYLE Simple
ARRANGEMENT Alternate
THORN Absent
LENGTH More than 5 cm
WIDTH 1.5 to 5 cm

FLOWER
COLOUR White/Cream
AROMA Yes
SIZE Less than 1 cm

FRUIT
COLOUR Black
SIZE 1 to 3 cm
TYPE Berry

DESCRIPTION	A medium sized evergreen tree growing up to a height of 10 metres, with smooth bark and no thorns.
HABITAT	Mature specimens are often found in undisturbed forest remnants, however it can also be found in degraded areas in a modified form.
LANDSCAPE INFORMATION	It is drought tolerant, has evergreen foliage, and is slow-growing.
PROPAGATION	Soak seeds for 12 hours, then sow in bags or beds. Early-ripe fruits have higher germination.
USES	The wood is called ebony and is used as a valuable timber for furniture, musical and agricultural instruments, and utensils.

GT   10–14 days
GR   High

Diospyros ferrea var. buxifolia | EBENACEAE

NAMES Ironwood (c)/ Irumbili (t)/ Angaru (h)

LEAF
- STYLE Simple
- ARRANGEMENT Alternate
- THORN Absent
- LENGTH 1 to 3 cm
- WIDTH 0.5 to 1.5 cm

FLOWER
- COLOUR White/Cream
- AROMA Yes
- SIZE Less than 1 cm

FRUIT
- COLOUR Red
- SIZE Less than 1 cm
- TYPE Berry

DESCRIPTION
: A small evergreen tree growing up to a height of 6 metres, with smooth bark and no thorns. Also known as *Diospyros vera*.

HABITAT
: Mature trees are often found in forest remnants that are less disturbed, however it can also be found in degraded areas as a shrub.

LANDSCAPE INFORMATION
: It is drought tolerant and is slow-growing. Listed as endangered on the IUCN Red List.

PROPAGATION
: Clean and soak seeds for 12 hours, then sow directly in bags or beds.

GT 10–14 days
GR High

USES
: The wood is used for making boat anchors, handles and rafters, and the fruit is edible.

Diospyros melanoxylon | EBENACEAE

NAMES Coromandel ebony (c)/ Thumbili (T)/ Tendu (H)

LEAF	
STYLE	Simple
ARRANGEMENT	Alternate
THORN	Absent
LENGTH	More than 5 cm
WIDTH	More than 5 cm

FLOWER	
COLOUR	White/Cream
AROMA	Yes
SIZE	Less than 1 cm

FRUIT	
COLOUR	Orange
SIZE	3 to 5 cm
TYPE	Berry

DESCRIPTION A medium sized deciduous tree growing up to a height of 10 metres, with rough bark and no thorns.

HABITAT This tree enjoys the full sun. It is found on hillocks, or in disturbed areas.

LANDSCAPE INFORMATION It is a good component in ecological landscaping.

PROPAGATION Clean and soak seeds for 12 hours, then sow directly in bags or beds. Very slow growth in nursery.

GT 30 days
GR Medium

USES The dried flowers have been used as a treatment for urinary, skin and blood diseases. The leaves are used as a wrapper for beedi in some states of India.

Diospyros montana | EBENACEAE

NAMES   Mottled ebony (c)/ Karundhuvalisu (т)/ Bistendu (н)

LEAF
STYLE Simple
ARRANGEMENT Alternate
THORN Absent
LENGTH More than 5 cm
WIDTH 1.5 to 5 cm

FLOWER
COLOUR Green
AROMA Yes
SIZE Less than 1 cm

FRUIT
COLOUR Yellow
SIZE 3 to 5 cm
TYPE Berry

DESCRIPTION   A medium sized deciduous tree growing up to a height of 10 metres, with smooth bark and no thorns.

HABITAT   This tree enjoys the full sun. It is often found in disturbed areas, and grows well on clay soils.

LANDSCAPE INFORMATION   It attracts bees, is slow-growing, and it is drought tolerant.

PROPAGATION   Clean and soak seeds for 12 hours, then sow directly in bags or beds. It remains dormant for a few months if sown in the summer.

USES   The fruits are poisonous, but have been used externally in the treatment of boils and spider stings.

GT   10 days
GR   Medium

Putranjiva roxburghii | PUTRANJIVACEAE

NAMES   Lucky bean tree (c)/ Puthirajeevi (T)/ Putijia (H)

 LEAF
STYLE Simple
ARRANGEMENT Alternate
THORN Absent
LENGTH More than 5 cm
WIDTH 1.5 to 5 cm

FLOWER
COLOUR White/Cream
AROMA Yes
SIZE Less than 1 cm

FRUIT
COLOUR Yellow
SIZE 1 to 3 cm
TYPE Drupe

DESCRIPTION	A medium sized evergreen tree growing up to a height of 10 metres, with smooth bark and no thorns.
HABITAT	This plant is generally found by rivers, or near to water bodies.
LANDSCAPE INFORMATION	This tree has pendant branches, is slow-growing, and is drought tolerant.
PROPAGATION	Crack seeds and soak for 24 hours, then sow in beds or trays.
USES	The leaves and fruits are used to treat colds, fevers, rheumatism and liver complaints. Necklaces of seeds are used for protection.

GT   10–14 days
GR   Medium

Atalantia monophylla | RUTACEAE

NAMES Wild lemon (c)/ Kaattu elumitchai (т)/
Bannimbu (н)/ Absence of desire (м)

LEAF
STYLE Simple
ARRANGEMENT Alternate
THORN Straight
LENGTH 3 to 5 cm
WIDTH 1.5 to 5 cm

FLOWER
COLOUR White/Cream
AROMA Yes
SIZE 1 to 3 cm

FRUIT
COLOUR Green
SIZE 1 to 2 cm
TYPE Berry

DESCRIPTION A medium sized evergreen tree growing up to a height of 10 metres, with smooth bark and thorns found on young growth.

HABITAT Mature trees are more often found in remnants that are less disturbed, however it is also found in degraded areas as a shrub.

LANDSCAPE INFORMATION This tree is a good hedge plant, is drought tolerant, and is slow-growing.

PROPAGATION Clean seeds and sow directly in bags or beds. Sprinkle with wood ash to stop caterpillars.

GT 10 days
GR High

USES The fruit oil has been used for chronic rheumatism. The fruit is used to make pickle.

Pamburus missionis | RUTACEAE

NAMES Wild orange (C)/ Kattu naarathal (T)

LEAF	
STYLE Simple	
ARRANGEMENT Alternate	
THORN Straight	
LENGTH More than 5 cm	
WIDTH 1.5 to 5 cm	

FLOWER	
COLOUR White/Cream	
AROMA Yes	
SIZE 1 to 3 cm	

FRUIT	
COLOUR Yellow	
SIZE 2 to 3 cm	
TYPE Berry	

DESCRIPTION	A medium sized evergreen tree growing up to a height of 10 metres, with rough bark and thorns found on young growth.
HABITAT	Mature specimens are mostly found in undisturbed forest remnants, however it can also be found in degraded areas in a modified form.
LANDSCAPE INFORMATION	It is slow-growing, and is drought tolerant.
PROPAGATION	Clean and soak seeds for 6 hours, then sow in beds or trays.
USES	The aerial parts have been used in the treatment of swelling, rheumatism and paralysis. The wood is used for handicrafts.

GT 21–30 days

GR Medium

Salvadora persica | SALVADORACEAE

NAMES   Toothbrush tree (C)/ Ugah (T)/ Jaal (H)

LEAF
STYLE Simple
ARRANGEMENT Opposite
THORN Absent
LENGTH 3 to 5 cm
WIDTH 1.5 to 5 cm

FLOWER
COLOUR White/Cream
AROMA No
SIZE Less than 1 cm

FRUIT
COLOUR Pink
SIZE Less than 1 cm
TYPE Drupe

DESCRIPTION   A small deciduous tree growing up to a height of 6 metres, with rough bark and no thorns.

HABITAT   This tree is found in coastal areas, or on black cotton soil. It is also tolerant of saline conditions.

LANDSCAPE INFORMATION   This is a beautiful, slow-growing tree.

PROPAGATION   Clean and soak seeds for 12 hours, then sow in beds or trays. Needs sun after transplanting.

USES   The leaf juice has been applied externally for rheumatism.

GT   5–10 days
GR   High

Madhuca longifolia | SAPOTACEAE

NAMES Indian butter tree (c)/ Kaattu yeluppai (t)/ Mahua (h)

LEAF
STYLE Simple
ARRANGEMENT Alternate
THORN Absent
LENGTH More than 5 cm
WIDTH More than 5 cm

FLOWER
COLOUR White/Cream
AROMA Yes
SIZE Less than 1 cm

FRUIT
COLOUR Green
SIZE 3 to 5 cm
TYPE Berry

DESCRIPTION	A large, spreading evergreen tree growing over 10 metres in height, with smooth bark and no thorns.
HABITAT	This plant is occasionally found in forest areas, however it is more usually found by the side of the road, on tank bunds, or in agricultural boundaries.
LANDSCAPE INFORMATION	This is a beautiful, slow-growing tree.
PROPAGATION	Clean and soak seeds for 12 hours, then sow directly in bags or beds.
USES	The fruits and flowers are edible. The seed oil is used for sacred lamps, and the wood is used for agricultural implements, temple carts and boats.

GT 21–30 days
GR High

Madhuca longifolia var. latifolia | SAPOTACEAE

NAMES Honey tree (c)/ Naati iluppai (t)/ Mahua (h)

LEAF
STYLE Simple
ARRANGEMENT Alternate
THORN Absent
LENGTH More than 5 cm
WIDTH More than 5 cm

FLOWER
COLOUR White/Cream
AROMA Yes
SIZE 1 to 3 cm

FRUIT
COLOUR Green
SIZE 3 to 5 cm
TYPE Berry

DESCRIPTION	A large, spreading evergreen tree growing over 10 metres in height, with smooth bark and no thorns.
HABITAT	This plant is occasionally found in forest areas, however it is more usually found by the side of the road, on tank bunds, or in agricultural boundaries.
LANDSCAPE INFORMATION	This is a beautiful, slow-growing tree.
PROPAGATION	Soak seeds for 12 hours, then sow directly in bags or beds.
USES	Leaves made into a paste have been used for stinging and itching problems of the skin. The wood is used for agricultural and temple equipment.

GT 21–30 days
GR High

Manilkara hexandra | SAPOTACEAE

NAMES   Ceylon rosewood (C)/ Kanupala (T)/ Khinni (H)

LEAF
STYLE Simple
ARRANGEMENT Alternate
THORN Absent
LENGTH More than 5 cm
WIDTH 1.5 to 5 cm

FLOWER
COLOUR White/Cream
AROMA Yes
SIZE Less than 1 cm

FRUIT
COLOUR Yellow
SIZE 1 to 3 cm
TYPE Berry

DESCRIPTION   A medium sized evergreen tree growing up to a height of 10 metres, with rough bark and no thorns.

HABITAT   Mature specimens are often found in undisturbed forest remnants, however it can also be found in degraded areas in a modified form.

LANDSCAPE INFORMATION   It is drought tolerant, has evergreen foliage, and is slow-growing.

PROPAGATION   Clean and soak seeds for 12 hours, then sow in beds or trays.

USES   Edible fruits. It is often used as a rootstock for the chikoo. The wood has timber value, where it is used for posts and pillars.

GT   30–60 days

GR   Medium to low

Mimusops elengi | SAPOTACEAE

NAMES   Bullet wood (c)/ Magizham (T)/ Maulsari (H)/ Patience (M)

LEAF		FLOWER		FRUIT	
STYLE Simple		**COLOUR** White/Cream		**COLOUR** Orange	
ARRANGEMENT Alternate		**AROMA** Yes		**SIZE** 1 to 3 cm	
THORN Absent		**SIZE** 1 to 3 cm		**TYPE** Berry	
LENGTH More than 5 cm					
WIDTH 1.5 to 5 cm					

DESCRIPTION

A medium sized evergreen tree growing up to a height of 10 m, with rough bark.

HABITAT

Mature specimens are often found in undisturbed forest remnants, however it can also be found in degraded areas in a modified form.

LANDSCAPE INFORMATION

It is drought tolerant, has evergreen foliage, and is slow-growing.

PROPAGATION

Clean seeds, scratch and soak for 12 hours, then sow directly in bags. Slow-growing in nursery.

USES

A decoction made from the bark is a good tonic, while leaves have been used to treat headaches, toothache, wounds and sore eyes.

GT   21–30 days

GR   Medium

Capparis brevispina | CAPPARACEAE

NAMES Indian caper (C)/ Kaattu aadhandai (T)/ Triple aspiration (M)

LEAF		FLOWER		FRUIT	
STYLE	Simple	COLOUR	White/Cream	COLOUR	Red
ARRANGEMENT	Alternate	AROMA	Yes	SIZE	3 to 5 cm
THORN	Recurved	SIZE	3 to 5 cm	TYPE	Berry
LENGTH	3 to 5 cm				
WIDTH	1.5 to 5 cm				

DESCRIPTION	An evergreen shrub, with smooth bark and thorns.
HABITAT	A shrub found mainly in disturbed areas, it can also be found on the edges of mature forest stands.
LANDSCAPE INFORMATION	It has beautiful flowers, and can be used as a garden feature.
PROPAGATION	Soak seeds for 12 hours, clean, then sow in beds or trays.
USES	It has edible fruits, and a pickle made from the fruit is reported to help with digestive complaints.

GT 7–10 days

GR Medium

Capparis divaricata | CAPPARACEAE

NAMES Spreading caper (C)/ Aadhandai (T)/ Pakhoda (H)

LEAF
STYLE Simple
ARRANGEMENT Alternate
THORN Recurved
LENGTH More than 5 cm
WIDTH 1.5 to 5 cm

FLOWER
COLOUR Yellow
AROMA Yes
SIZE 1 to 3 cm

FRUIT
COLOUR Red
SIZE 3 to 5 cm
TYPE Berry

DESCRIPTION A deciduous shrub, with rough bark and thorns.

HABITAT This shrub enjoys the full sun. It is generally found in disturbed areas, and is rarely found in mature forest stands.

LANDSCAPE INFORMATION It has beautiful flowers and it attracts butterflies and birds.

PROPAGATION Soak seeds for 12 hours, clean, then sow in beds or trays. Seedling aftercare required after transplanting.

GT 7–10 days
GR Medium

USES The unripe fruit can be made into a pickle which is reported to help with digestive ailments.

INDIAN OAK / *Neerkkadambai*
Barringtonia acutangula

PALA INDIGO / *Vetpaalai*
Wrightia tinctoria

Dimorphocalyx glabellus | EUPHORBIACEAE

NAMES Malaikkulukki (T)/ Jodpakli (H)

LEAF		FLOWER		FRUIT	
STYLE	Simple	COLOUR	White/Cream	COLOUR	Brown/Rusty
ARRANGEMENT	Alternate	AROMA	Yes	SIZE	3 to 5 cm
THORN	Absent	SIZE	1 to 3 cm	TYPE	Capsule
LENGTH	More than 5 cm				
WIDTH	1.5 to 5 cm				

DESCRIPTION   An evergreen shrub, with rough bark and no thorns.

HABITAT   This plant is normally found in the understorey of the forest, and only if the canopy has been recently removed will it be found in the open sun.

LANDSCAPE INFORMATION   It is drought tolerant, has beautiful foliage, and is relatively fast growing.

PROPAGATION   Clean and soak seeds for 12 hours, then sow directly in bags or beds.

USES   The leaves of this shrub are diuretic and purgative, and have been used in the treatment of dyspepsia and rheumatism.

   GT 10–14 days

GR High

Suregada angustifolia | EUPHORBIACEAE

NAMES South Indian suregada (c)/ Kakaipalai (T)

LEAF
STYLE Simple
ARRANGEMENT Alternate
THORN Absent
LENGTH More than 5 cm
WIDTH 1.5 to 5 cm

FLOWER
COLOUR White/Cream
AROMA No
SIZE Less than 1 cm

FRUIT
COLOUR Brown/Rusty
SIZE 1 to 2 cm
TYPE Capsule

DESCRIPTION
An evergreen shrub, with smooth bark and no thorns. Also known as *Suregada lanceolata*.

HABITAT
This shrub can be found in the open, or as a component of the understorey in a mature forest.

LANDSCAPE INFORMATION
It is drought tolerant, has beautiful foliage, and is relatively fast growing.

PROPAGATION
Clean and soak seeds for 12 hours, then sow in beds or trays.

USES
The seed paste has been used to treat leprosy, and the roots have been used to treat fever.

GT 7–10 days

GR Very High

Eugenia bracteata | MYRTACEAE

LEAF	**STYLE** Simple		**FLOWER**	**COLOUR** White/Cream		**FRUIT**	**COLOUR** Red
	ARRANGEMENT Opposite			**AROMA** Yes			**SIZE** Less than 1 cm
	THORN Absent			**SIZE** Less than 1 cm			**TYPE** Berry
	LENGTH 3 to 5 cm						
	WIDTH 1.5 to 5 cm						

DESCRIPTION	An evergreen shrub, with smooth bark and no thorns. Also known as *Eugenia roxburghii*.
HABITAT	This shrub can be found in coastal areas, on sandy soils, in the open, or as a component of the understorey in a mature forest.
LANDSCAPE INFORMATION	It is drought tolerant, has beautiful foliage, and is relatively fast growing.
PROPAGATION	Clean and soak seeds for 12 hours, then sow directly in bags or beds. Transplant early. Seedling aftercare required.
USES	The fruits are edible.

GT 40–60 days

GR Medium

Barringtonia acutangula | LECYTHIDACEAE

NAMES   Indian oak (c)/ Neerkkadambai (t)/ Hijjal (h)

LEAF
STYLE Simple
ARRANGEMENT Alternate
THORN Absent
LENGTH More than 5 cm
WIDTH More than 5 cm

FLOWER
COLOUR Red
AROMA Yes
SIZE 1 to 3 cm

FRUIT
COLOUR Brown/Rusty
SIZE 1 to 3 cm
TYPE Berry

DESCRIPTION	A medium sized deciduous tree growing up to a height of 10 metres, with rough bark and no thorns.
HABITAT	This tree is found mainly near water bodies, and commonly on heavy soils as it is tolerant of clay soil with poor drainage. It can also withstand seasonal waterlogging.
LANDSCAPE INFORMATION	It attracts bees, has evergreen foliage, is slow-growing and is drought tolerant.
PROPAGATION	Soak for 12 hours, then sow directly in bags.
USES	It is known as 'Dhatriphala' in Ayurvedic medicine. The wood is used for timber, and the leaf has been used as a fish poison.

GT   30 days
GR   High

Miliusa eriocarpa | ANNONACEAE

NAMES   Woolly-fruit miliusa (c)

LEAF	
STYLE	Simple
ARRANGEMENT	Alternate
THORN	Absent
LENGTH	3 to 5 cm
WIDTH	1.5 to 5 cm

FLOWER	
COLOUR	Red
AROMA	No
SIZE	1 to 3 cm

FRUIT	
COLOUR	Red
SIZE	Less than 1 cm
TYPE	Drupe

DESCRIPTION	An evergreen shrub, with rough bark and no thorns.
HABITAT	This shrub is normally found in the understorey of the forest, and only if the canopy has been recently removed will it be found in the open sun.
LANDSCAPE INFORMATION	It is drought tolerant, and is a good plant in semi-shade.
PROPAGATION	Clean and soak seeds for 12 hours, then sow in beds or trays.

GT	6 months
GR	High

Memecylon umbellatum | MELASTOMATACEAE

NAMES   Ironwood (C)/ Kaasan (T)/ Anjan (H)/ Miracle, air of Auroville (M)

LEAF
STYLE Simple
ARRANGEMENT Opposite
THORN Absent
LENGTH 3 to 5 cm
WIDTH 1.5 to 5 cm

FLOWER
COLOUR Blue
AROMA Yes
SIZE Less than 1 cm

FRUIT
COLOUR Purple/Blue
SIZE Less than 1 cm
TYPE Berry

DESCRIPTION   A small evergreen tree growing up to a height of 6 metres, with rough bark and no thorns.

HABITAT   Mature trees are more often found in forest remnants that are less disturbed, however also found in degraded areas as a shrub.

LANDSCAPE INFORMATION   It has beautiful flowers, and can be used as a garden feature.

PROPAGATION   Clean and soak seeds for 12 hours, then sow 4 seeds directly in each bag. Water with Panchagavya every 10 days.

 GT   10–14 days

 GR   Medium

USES   The leaves have been used as a treatment for venereal diseases. The wood is used for minor wood crafts.

Holoptelea integrifolia | ULMACEAE

NAMES Indian elm (C)/ Aaya (T)/ Chirhol (H)

LEAF
STYLE Simple
ARRANGEMENT Alternate
THORN Absent
LENGTH More than 5 cm
WIDTH 1.5 to 5 cm

FLOWER
COLOUR Green
AROMA No
SIZE Less than 1 cm

FRUIT
COLOUR Brown/Rusty
SIZE 3 to 5 cm
TYPE Capsule

DESCRIPTION A large, spreading deciduous tree growing over 10 metres, with rough bark and no thorns.

HABITAT This tree enjoys the full sun. It is a component of the deciduous forest type and is generally found in the hills.

LANDSCAPE INFORMATION This is a fast-growing tree, and is drought tolerant. It is good for creating an early canopy.

PROPAGATION Soak seeds overnight, then sow directly in beds.

USES The wood is a valuable timber. The bark has been used to treat rheumatism and skin diseases.

GT 2–4 weeks

GR Medium

Streblus asper | MORACEAE

NAMES   Sandpaper tree (c)/ Piraai (t)/ Daheya (h)

LEAF	
STYLE	Simple
ARRANGEMENT	Alternate
THORN	Absent
LENGTH	More than 5 cm
WIDTH	1.5 to 5 cm

FLOWER	
COLOUR	Green
AROMA	No
SIZE	Less than 1 cm

FRUIT	
COLOUR	Yellow
SIZE	Less than 1 cm
TYPE	Drupe

DESCRIPTION   A medium sized evergreen tree growing up to a height of 10 metres, with smooth bark and no thorns.

HABITAT   Mature specimens are often found in undisturbed forest remnants, however it can also be found in degraded areas in a modified form.

LANDSCAPE INFORMATION   It is drought tolerant, has evergreen foliage, and is slow-growing.

PROPAGATION   Clean seeds and sow directly in beds or trays. No need to soak.

USES   A decoction made from the bark has been used as a treatment for fever, diarrhoea and dysentery.

GT   7–10 days

GR   Medium

Drypetes porteri | PUTRANJIVACEAE

NAMES   Agil (T)

LEAF
STYLE Simple
ARRANGEMENT Alternate
THORN Absent
LENGTH More than 5 cm
WIDTH 1.5 to 5 cm

FLOWER
COLOUR Green
AROMA No
SIZE 1 to 3 cm

FRUIT
COLOUR Brown/Rusty
SIZE 1 to 3 cm
TYPE Drupe

DESCRIPTION   A medium sized evergreen tree growing up to a height of 10 metres, with smooth bark and no thorns.

HABITAT   This is a rare tree. It is found on hillocks and often associated with seasonal streams.

LANDSCAPE INFORMATION   It is drought tolerant, has evergreen foliage, and is slow-growing. Listed as endangered on the IUCN Red List.

PROPAGATION   Clean and soak seeds for 12 hours, then sow directly in bags or beds. Spray with copper sulphate against fungus.

GT   10–14 days
GR   High

USES   The fruits are used for fodder for goats and cows, and the wood is used by local craftsmen for the production of combs.

Drypetes sepiaria | PUTRANJIVACEAE

NAMES   Hedge boxwood (c)/ Veerai (т)

LEAF		FLOWER		FRUIT	
STYLE Simple		**COLOUR** Green		**COLOUR** Red	
ARRANGEMENT Alternate		**AROMA** Yes		**SIZE** Less than 1 cm	
THORN Absent		**SIZE** Less than 1 cm		**TYPE** Drupe	
LENGTH More than 5 cm					
WIDTH 1.5 to 5 cm					

DESCRIPTION   A medium sized evergreen tree growing up to a height of 10 metres, with smooth bark and no thorns.

HABITAT   Mature specimens are often found in undisturbed forest remnants, however it can also be found in degraded areas in a modified form.

LANDSCAPE INFORMATION   It is drought tolerant, has evergreen foliage, and is slow-growing.

PROPAGATION   Clean and soak seeds for 12 hours, then sow directly in bags or beds. Use 2–3 seeds per bag and place it in semi-shade.

GT   21–30 days

GR   Medium

USES   The fruits and seeds are edible, and it is used for fencing and firewood.

Polyalthia coffeoides | ANNONACEAE

NAMES   Coffee ashok (c)/ Nedunaarai (т)/
Ashok (н)

LEAF
STYLE Simple
ARRANGEMENT Alternate
THORN Absent
LENGTH More than 5 cm
WIDTH 0.5 to 1 cm

FLOWER
COLOUR Green
AROMA No
SIZE 1 to 3 cm

FRUIT
COLOUR Red
SIZE Less than 1 cm
TYPE Drupe

DESCRIPTION   An evergreen shrub, with smooth bark and no
thorns. Also known as *Monoon coffeoides*.

HABITAT   This shrub can be found in the open, or as a
component of the understorey in a mature forest.

LANDSCAPE   It is a beautiful evergreen shrub, with great form
INFORMATION   and attractive fruit.

PROPAGATION   Clean and soak seeds for 24 hours, then sow
in beds.

GT   60–90 days
GR   Medium

USES   The fruits are edible for langurs and fruit bats.
The fibre from the bark is made into ropes.

Polyalthia korinti | ANNONACEAE

NAMES Sirunetti (T)

LEAF
STYLE Simple
ARRANGEMENT Alternate
THORN Absent
LENGTH More than 5 cm
WIDTH 1.5 to 5 cm

FLOWER
COLOUR Green
AROMA No
SIZE 1 to 3 cm

FRUIT
COLOUR Red
SIZE Less than 1 cm
TYPE Drupe

DESCRIPTION An evergreen shrub, with smooth bark and no thorns.

HABITAT This shrub is normally found in the understorey, and only if the canopy is recently removed is it found in the open sun.

LANDSCAPE INFORMATION It is drought tolerant, and is a good plant for landscaping in the semi-shade.

PROPAGATION Clean and soak seeds for 12 hours, then sow in beds or trays.

USES The fruits are edible. The wood is hard and durable, but usually too small for most carpentry purposes.

GT 60–90 days
GR Medium

Polyalthia suberosa | ANNONACEAE

NAMES Corky debbar tree (c)/ Kaattu netti (t)/ Cham-khirni (h)

LEAF		FLOWER		FRUIT	
STYLE	Simple	COLOUR	Yellow	COLOUR	Purple/Blue
ARRANGEMENT	Alternate	AROMA	No	SIZE	Less than 1 cm
THORN	Absent	SIZE	1 to 3 cm	TYPE	Drupe
LENGTH	3 to 5 cm				
WIDTH	1.5 to 5 cm				

DESCRIPTION	An evergreen shrub, with smooth bark and no thorns.
HABITAT	This shrub is normally found in the understorey of the forest or in shady hedgerows, and only if the canopy has been recently removed will it be found in the open sun.
LANDSCAPE INFORMATION	It is drought tolerant, has beautiful foliage, and is relatively fast growing.
PROPAGATION	Clean and soak seeds for 24 hours, then sow in beds or trays.
USES	The fruit is edible. The wood is used in carpentry, and in the masts and spars of small boats.

GT 60–90 days

GR Medium

Hibiscus tiliaceus | MALVACEAE

NAMES   Beach hibiscus (C)/ Neer paruththi (T)

LEAF
- **STYLE** Simple
- **ARRANGEMENT** Alternate
- **THORN** Absent
- **LENGTH** More than 5 cm
- **WIDTH** More than 5 cm

FLOWER
- **COLOUR** Yellow
- **AROMA** Yes
- **SIZE** 3 to 5 cm

FRUIT
- **COLOUR** Brown/Rusty
- **SIZE** 3 to 5 cm
- **TYPE** Capsule

DESCRIPTION	A small evergreen tree growing up to a height of 6 metres, with smooth bark and no thorns.
HABITAT	This tree is generally found in coastal areas, often behind mangrove forests. Commonly planted in villages for shade.
LANDSCAPE INFORMATION	It is a coastal species with beautiful flowers, is relatively fast growing, and is drought tolerant.
PROPAGATION	Clean and soak seeds for 12 hours, then sow in beds or trays. Can propagate from cuttings.
USES	The wood is used for seacraft construction and wood carving. The stem fibres make good ropes.

GT   1–2 months

GR   Medium

Hugonia mystax | LINACEAE

NAMES Climbing wax (C)/ Mothirakanni (T)/ Kamsamarah (H)

LEAF
STYLE Simple
ARRANGEMENT Alternate
THORN Absent
LENGTH 1 to 3 cm
WIDTH 0.5 to 1.5 cm

FLOWER
COLOUR Yellow
AROMA Yes
SIZE 1 to 3 cm

FRUIT
COLOUR Red
SIZE 1 to 3 cm
TYPE Drupe

DESCRIPTION	An evergreen straggler, with smooth bark and no thorns.
HABITAT	This plant is found either in mature stands reaching up into the canopy, or in more disturbed areas straggling over other plants.
LANDSCAPE INFORMATION	As a climber, this plant can be used for covering walls.
PROPAGATION	Clean, crack and soak seeds for 30 min, then sow in trays. Aftercare required once transplanted.
USES	The root paste has been used externally to reduce inflamed swelling.

GT 30 days
GR Low

Alangium salviifolium | CORNACEAE

NAMES Sage-leaved alangium (c)/ Azhinjil (T)/
Ankol (H)

LEAF
STYLE Simple
ARRANGEMENT Alternate
THORN Absent
LENGTH More than 5 cm
WIDTH 1.5 to 5 cm

FLOWER
COLOUR White/Cream
AROMA Yes
SIZE 1 to 3 cm

FRUIT
COLOUR Red
SIZE 3 to 5 cm
TYPE Berry

DESCRIPTION A medium sized deciduous tree growing up to a
height of 10 metres, with rough bark and no thorns.

HABITAT This tree is occasionally found in forest areas,
however it is more usually found by the side of the
road, on tank bunds, or in agricultural boundaries.

LANDSCAPE
INFORMATION It attracts birds, is slow-growing, and is drought
tolerant.

PROPAGATION Soak for 12 hours, then clean and sow directly
in bags.

 GT 30 days
 GR High

USES The leaves have been used to treat rheumatic pain,
a root decoction for fever and skin diseases, and the
root and bark for skin problems.

Pterospermum suberifolium | MALVACEAE

NAMES Cork-leaved bayur (c)/ Vennangu (T)

LEAF	**STYLE** Simple	**FLOWER**	**COLOUR** White/Cream	**FRUIT**	**COLOUR** Brown/Rusty
	ARRANGEMENT Alternate		**AROMA** Yes		**SIZE** More than 5 cm
	THORN Absent		**SIZE** More than 5 cm		**TYPE** Capsule
	LENGTH More than 5 cm				
	WIDTH 1.5 to 5 cm				

DESCRIPTION	A medium sized brevideciduous tree growing up to a height of 10 metres, with smooth bark and no thorns.
HABITAT	Mature specimens are often found in undisturbed forest remnants, however it can also be found in degraded areas in a modified form.
LANDSCAPE INFORMATION	It is drought tolerant, has beautiful foliage, and is relatively fast growing.
PROPAGATION	Clean and soak seeds for 24 hours, then sow in beds or trays.
USES	The flower is made into a paste with rice water, and has been used as an application for chronic headaches.

GT 10–14 days

GR High

Pterospermum xylocarpum | MALVACEAE

NAMES   Tada (c)/ Pulavu (T)

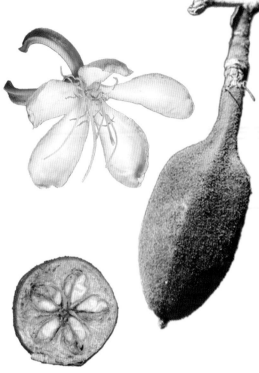

LEAF
STYLE Simple
ARRANGEMENT Alternate
THORN Absent
LENGTH More than 5 cm
WIDTH More than 5 cm

FLOWER
COLOUR White/Cream
AROMA Yes
SIZE More than 5 cm

FRUIT
COLOUR Brown/Rusty
SIZE More than 5 cm
TYPE Capsule

DESCRIPTION   A medium sized tree growing up to a height of 10 metres, brevideciduous, with smooth bark and no thorns.

HABITAT   Mature specimens are generally found on the hillocks, and occasionally on the plains as part of a mature forest.

LANDSCAPE INFORMATION   It is drought tolerant, has beautiful foliage, and is relatively fast growing.

PROPAGATION   Clean and soak seeds for 24 hours, then sow in beds or trays.

USES   The leaves and flowers have been used to treat vaginal discharge, and the bark has been used to treat asthma.

GT   10–14 days
GR   High

Ficus albipila | MORACEAE

NAMES   Abbey tree (c)

LEAF		FLOWER		FRUIT	
STYLE	Simple	COLOUR	Green	COLOUR	Pink
ARRANGEMENT	Alternate	AROMA	No	SIZE	Less than 1 cm
THORN	Absent	SIZE	Less than 1 cm	TYPE	Fig
LENGTH	More than 5 cm				
WIDTH	More than 5 cm				

DESCRIPTION   A medium sized deciduous tree growing up to a height of 10 metres, with smooth bark and no thorns.

HABITAT   This tree is found on the hillocks, growing in between the rocks, where good soil has accumulated.

LANDSCAPE INFORMATION   It is a good component in ecological landscaping.

PROPAGATION   Clean seeds and spread in trays. Keep moist and transplant only after a few leaves appear. Spray copper sulphate against fungus.

GT   10–14 days

GR   Medium to low

USES   The wood is used for house construction.

Ficus amplissima | MORACEAE

NAMES Indian bat tree (c)/ Kal ichi (т)/ Piparee (н)

LEAF
STYLE Simple
ARRANGEMENT Alternate
THORN Absent
LENGTH More than 5 cm
WIDTH More than 5 cm

FLOWER
COLOUR Green
AROMA No
SIZE Less than 1 cm

FRUIT
COLOUR Black
SIZE Less than 1 cm
TYPE Fig

DESCRIPTION — A large, spreading brevideciduous tree growing over 10 metres in height, with smooth bark and no thorns.

HABITAT — This tree is occasionally found in forest areas, however it is more usually found by the side of the road, on tank bunds, or in agricultural edges.

LANDSCAPE INFORMATION — It is drought tolerant, has beautiful foliage, and is relatively fast growing.

PROPAGATION — Clean seeds and spread in trays, always keeping them moist. Transplant only after a few leaves appear. Spray copper sulphate against fungus. Requires half sun.

GT 10–14 days
GR Medium to low

USES — The fruit is edible. The latex has been used for fresh wounds.

BANYAN / *Aala maram*
Ficus benghalensis

Ficus arnottiana | MORACEAE

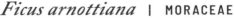

NAMES   Indian rock fig (c)/ Kodi arasu (T)/
Bassari (H)

LEAF		FLOWER		FRUIT	
STYLE	Simple	COLOUR	Green	COLOUR	Purple/Blue
ARRANGEMENT	Alternate	AROMA	No	SIZE	Less than 1 cm
THORN	Absent	SIZE	Less than 1 cm	TYPE	Fig
LENGTH	More than 5 cm				
WIDTH	More than 5 cm				

DESCRIPTION   A medium sized deciduous tree growing up to a height of 10 metres, with smooth bark and no thorns.

HABITAT   This tree enjoys the full sun, and is generally found on hillocks in open areas.

LANDSCAPE INFORMATION   It is drought tolerant and is relatively fast growing. Distinguished from the Peepal by its bright pink veins and leaf stalk.

PROPAGATION   Clean seeds and spread in trays, always keeping them moist. Transplant only after a few leaves appear. Spray copper sulphate against fungus. Requires half sun.

GT   10–14 days
GR   Low

USES   The leaves and bark are used for skin diseases, cuts and wounds.

Ficus benghalensis | **MORACEAE**

NAMES   Banyan (c)/ Aala maram (T)/ Barh (H)

LEAF
STYLE Simple
ARRANGEMENT Alternate
THORN Absent
LENGTH More than 5 cm
WIDTH More than 5 cm

FLOWER
COLOUR Green
AROMA No
SIZE Less than 1 cm

FRUIT
COLOUR Red
SIZE 1 to 3 cm
TYPE Fig

DESCRIPTION   A large, spreading brevideciduous tree growing over 10 metres in height, with smooth bark and no thorns.

HABITAT   This tree is occasionally found in forest areas, however it is more usually found by the side of the road.

LANDSCAPE INFORMATION   It has a large, spreading canopy and is good for planting in a park.

PROPAGATION   Clean seeds and spread in trays, always keeping them moist. Transplant only after a few leaves appear. Spray copper sulphate against fungus. Requires half sun. Can propagate from cuttings.

GT   10–14 days

GR   Medium to low

USES   The bark has reported tonic, astringent and cooling properties.

Ficus hispida | MORACEAE

NAMES Hairy fig (C)/ Peyathi (T)/ Gobla (H)

LEAF	**STYLE** Simple	**FLOWER**	**COLOUR** Green	**FRUIT**	**COLOUR** Yellow
	ARRANGEMENT Alternate and Decussate		**AROMA** No		**SIZE** 1 to 3 cm
	THORN Absent		**SIZE** Less than 1 cm		**TYPE** Fig
	LENGTH More than 5 cm				
	WIDTH More than 5 cm				

DESCRIPTION A deciduous shrub, with smooth bark and no thorns.

HABITAT This plant is occasionally found in forest areas, however it is more usually found by the side of the road or on tank bunds.

LANDSCAPE INFORMATION It is fast growing, and is good for creating an early canopy.

PROPAGATION Clean seeds and spread in trays, always keeping them moist. Transplant only after a few leaves appear. Spray copper sulphate against fungus. Requires half sun.

GT 10–14 days

GR Medium to low

USES The unripe fruits are cooked and the bark fibre is used for cordage. The fruits have been used traditionally to treat cow intestinal worms.

Ficus microcarpa | MORACEAE

NAMES Chinese banyan (c)/ Kalichchi (t)

LEAF
STYLE Simple
ARRANGEMENT Alternate
THORN Absent
LENGTH More than 5 cm
WIDTH 1.5 to 5 cm

FLOWER
COLOUR Green
AROMA No
SIZE Less than 1 cm

FRUIT
COLOUR Orange
SIZE Less than 1 cm
TYPE Fig

DESCRIPTION A medium sized tree growing up to 10 metres, brevideciduous, with smooth bark and no thorns.

HABITAT This tree is generally found on the hillocks, either amongst open rocks, or as part of a mixed forest.

LANDSCAPE INFORMATION This is an interesting tree to include in a landscape as it has unique characteristics.

PROPAGATION Clean seeds and spread in trays, always keeping them moist. Transplant only after a few leaves appear. Spray copper sulphate against fungus. Requires half sun.

GT 10–14 days
GR Low

USES Remedies made from this plant have been used to treat pain, fever, flu, malaria, bronchitis and rheumatism.

Ficus mollis | MORACEAE

NAMES Soft fig (c)/ Kaattu aal (T)

LEAF		FLOWER		FRUIT	
STYLE	Simple	COLOUR	Brown	COLOUR	Grey
ARRANGEMENT	Alternate	AROMA	No	SIZE	Less than 1 cm
THORN	Absent	SIZE	Less than 1 cm	TYPE	Fig
LENGTH	More than 5 cm				
WIDTH	More than 5 cm				

DESCRIPTION	A medium sized deciduous tree growing up to a height of 10 metres, with smooth bark and no thorns.		
HABITAT	This tree enjoys the full sun. It is found on hillocks, often at the top, or by exposed rock.		
LANDSCAPE INFORMATION	It is drought tolerant, has beautiful foliage, and is relatively fast growing.		
PROPAGATION	Clean seeds and spread in trays, always keeping them moist. Transplant only after a few leaves appear. Spray copper sulphate against fungus. Requires half sun.	GT	10–14 days
		GR	Medium to low
USES	The latex is used medicinally. The crushed leaves have been used to treat boils, and the bark paste has been used for cuts and wounds.		

Ficus racemosa | MORACEAE

NAMES   Cluster fig tree (c)/ Vellai athi (T)/ Gular (H)

LEAF	**STYLE** Simple	**FLOWER**	**COLOUR** Green	**FRUIT**	**COLOUR** Red	

LEAF
STYLE Simple
ARRANGEMENT Alternate
THORN Absent
LENGTH More than 5 cm
WIDTH 1.5 to 5 cm

FLOWER
COLOUR Green
AROMA No
SIZE Less than 1 cm

FRUIT
COLOUR Red
SIZE 1 to 3 cm
TYPE Fig

DESCRIPTION	A medium sized deciduous tree growing up to a height of 10 metres, with smooth bark and no thorns. Also known as *Ficus glomerata*.
HABITAT	This plant is occasionally found in forest areas, however it is more usually found by the side of the road or on tank bunds.
LANDSCAPE INFORMATION	It is drought tolerant and slow-growing.
PROPAGATION	Clean seeds and spread in trays, always keeping them moist. Transplant only after a few leaves appear. Use copper sulphate to prevent fungus in trays. Half sun.
USES	The fruits are edible, and the seeds are used to treat menstrual pain.

GT   10–14 days
GR   Medium to low

Ficus religiosa | MORACEAE

NAMES   Bodhi tree (C)/ Arasa maram (T)/ Peepal (H)

LEAF
STYLE Simple
ARRANGEMENT Alternate
THORN Absent
LENGTH More than 5 cm
WIDTH More than 5 cm

FLOWER
COLOUR Green
AROMA No
SIZE Less than 1 cm

FRUIT
COLOUR Purple/Blue
SIZE 0.5 to 1.5 cm
TYPE Fig

DESCRIPTION	A large, spreading deciduous tree growing over 10 metres in height, with rough bark and no thorns.
HABITAT	This tree is occasionally found in forest areas, however it is more usually found by the side of the road.
LANDSCAPE INFORMATION	It is drought tolerant, has beautiful foliage, and is relatively fast growing.
PROPAGATION	Clean seeds and spread in trays, always keeping them moist. Transplant only after a few leaves appear. Spray copper sulphate against fungus. Requires half sun.
USES	The bark is used to treat eczema and the milk is applied externally to treat foot cracks.

GT   10–14 days

GR   Medium to low

Ficus tinctoria subsp. gibbosa | MORACEAE

NAMES Dye fig (c)/ Kallathi (t)

LEAF	**STYLE** Simple	**FLOWER**	**COLOUR** Green	**FRUIT**	**COLOUR** Orange
	ARRANGEMENT Alternate		**AROMA** No		**SIZE** 1 to 3 cm
	THORN Absent		**SIZE** Less than 1 cm		**TYPE** Fig
	LENGTH More than 5 cm				
	WIDTH 1.5 to 5 cm				

DESCRIPTION A medium sized deciduous tree growing up to a height of 10 metres, with smooth bark and no thorns. Also known as *Ficus tinctoria subsp. parasitica.*

HABITAT This tree is occasionally found in forest areas, however it is more usually found by the side of the road.

LANDSCAPE INFORMATION It is slow-growing and drought tolerant.

PROPAGATION Clean seeds and spread in trays, always keeping them moist. Transplant only after a few leaves appear. Use copper sulphate to prevent fungus in trays. Requires half sun.

GT 10–14 days

GR Medium to low

USES The fruit is the source of a red fabric dye. The young shoots are eaten cooked or roasted.

Careya arborea | LECYTHIDACEAE

NAMES Wild guava (c)/ Pezhai maram (t)/ Khumai (h)/ Liberation (m)

LEAF
STYLE Simple
ARRANGEMENT Alternate
THORN Absent
LENGTH More than 5 cm
WIDTH More than 5 cm

FLOWER
COLOUR White/Cream
AROMA Yes
SIZE More than 5 cm

FRUIT
COLOUR Green
SIZE More than 5 cm
TYPE Berry

DESCRIPTION A medium sized deciduous tree growing up to a height of 10 metres, with rough bark and no thorns.

HABITAT This tree enjoys full sun, is a component of the deciduous forest type, and is rarely found in mature evergreen stands.

LANDSCAPE INFORMATION This is an interesting tree to include in a landscape.

PROPAGATION Extract seeds from fruit, soak for 12 hours and sow in beds. Likes sun after transplanting.

USES The juice made from the flowers is used for coughs and colds. The bark has been used to treat snakebites.

GT 30 days
GR Medium

Carmona retusa | BORAGINACEAE

NAMES Fukien tea (c)/ Kurangu vetrilai (т)/ Pala (н)

LEAF
STYLE Simple
ARRANGEMENT Alternate
THORN Absent
LENGTH 1 to 3 cm
WIDTH 0.5 to 1.5 cm

FLOWER
COLOUR White/Cream
AROMA No
SIZE Less than 1 cm

FRUIT
COLOUR Brown/Rusty
SIZE Less than 1 cm
TYPE Drupe

DESCRIPTION A deciduous shrub, with smooth bark and no thorns. Also known as *Ehretia microphylla*.

HABITAT This shrub can be found in the open, or as a component of the understorey in a mature forest.

LANDSCAPE INFORMATION It is drought tolerant and attracts butterflies. It can be grown as a hedge and for bonsai.

PROPAGATION Clean seeds and soak for 12 hours, then sow in trays.

USES A decoction of the leaves has been used to treat dysentery and indigestion.

GT 60–90 days
GR High

Ehretia pubescens | BORAGINACEAE

NAMES   Aadali (c)/ Chamror (H)

LEAF
STYLE Simple
ARRANGEMENT Alternate
THORN Absent
LENGTH 3 to 7 cm
WIDTH 1.5 to 5 cm

FLOWER
COLOUR White/Cream
AROMA Yes
SIZE Less than 1 cm

FRUIT
COLOUR Red
SIZE Less than 1 cm
TYPE Drupe

DESCRIPTION   A small deciduous tree growing up to a height of 6 metres, with smooth bark and no thorns. Also known as *Ehretia laevis*.

HABITAT   This tree enjoys full sun. It is found in disturbed areas, but also in the understorey of mature stands.

LANDSCAPE INFORMATION   It attracts birds, and is drought tolerant.

PROPAGATION   Clean and dry seeds, then sow in beds with a light soil covering. Sprinkle with wood ash to stop caterpillars.

GT   7–10 days
GR   Medium

USES   A decoction made from the roots has been used to treat venereal diseases.

Erythroxylum monogynum | ERYTHROXYLACEAE

NAMES Bastard sandal (c)/ Sembulichan (т)

LEAF
STYLE Simple
ARRANGEMENT Alternate
THORN Absent
LENGTH 1.5 to 3 cm
WIDTH 0.5 to 1.5 cm

FLOWER
COLOUR White/Cream
AROMA No
SIZE 1 to 3 cm

FRUIT
COLOUR Red
SIZE Less than 1 cm
TYPE Drupe

DESCRIPTION An evergreen shrub, with smooth bark and no thorns.

HABITAT This shrub can be found in the open, or as a component of the understorey in a mature forest.

LANDSCAPE INFORMATION This shrub attracts birds. It is beautiful and drought tolerant.

PROPAGATION Clean and soak seeds overnight, then sow in trays. Often the seeds collected are sterile.

GT 1 month
GR Low

USES The leaves and fruit are edible. This plant has been used medicinally for stomach upsets and fever. It also yields an essential and a wood oil.

Maytenus emarginata | CELASTRACEAE

NAMES Thorny staff tree (c)/ Vedippula (T)/ Baikal (H)

LEAF		FLOWER		FRUIT	
STYLE	Simple	COLOUR	White/Cream	COLOUR	Brown/Rusty
ARRANGEMENT	Alternate	AROMA	Yes	SIZE	1 to 3 cm
THORN	Straight	SIZE	Less than 1 cm	TYPE	Capsule
LENGTH	3 to 7 cm				
WIDTH	1.5 to 5 cm				

DESCRIPTION	A deciduous shrub, with smooth bark and thorns. Also known as *Gymnosporia emarginata*.	
HABITAT	This shrub is found mainly in disturbed areas. It grows in the full sun, and disappears if the canopy closes.	
LANDSCAPE INFORMATION	It is drought tolerant, and attracts butterflies.	
PROPAGATION	Clean and soak seeds for 12 hours, then sow in beds or trays.	GT 2 weeks GR High
USES	This shrub is good as a living fence.	

Mallotus philippensis | EUPHORBIACEAE

NAMES Red kamala (C)/ Kunguma maram (T)/ Kamala (H)

LEAF
- **STYLE** Simple
- **ARRANGEMENT** Alternate
- **THORN** Absent
- **LENGTH** More than 5 cm
- **WIDTH** More than 5 cm

FLOWER
- **COLOUR** Red
- **AROMA** No
- **SIZE** Less than 1 cm

FRUIT
- **COLOUR** Red
- **SIZE** Less than 1 cm
- **TYPE** Capsule

DESCRIPTION	A deciduous shrub, with smooth bark and no thorns.
HABITAT	This shrub enjoys the full sun. It is found in disturbed areas, and rarely found in mature evergreen stands.
LANDSCAPE INFORMATION	It is drought tolerant and fast growing. Its beautiful foliage is good for creating an early canopy.
PROPAGATION	Clean and soak seeds for 12 hours, then sow in beds or trays. Suffers during transplantation.
USES	The glandular hairs from the fruits yield a golden red colour dye. The seed oil is used in paints and varnishes.

GT 21–30 days

GR Medium

Mallotus rhamnifolius | EUPHORBIACEAE

NAMES   Buckthorn-leaved kamala (c)/ Marai yirdiyam (T)

LEAF
STYLE Simple
ARRANGEMENT Alternate
THORN Absent
LENGTH More than 5 cm
WIDTH 1.5 to 5 cm

FLOWER
COLOUR White/Cream
AROMA No
SIZE Less than 1 cm

FRUIT
COLOUR Brown/Rusty
SIZE Less than 1 cm
TYPE Capsule

DESCRIPTION	A deciduous shrub, with smooth bark and no thorns.
HABITAT	This shrub can be found in the open, or as a component of the understorey in a mature forest.
LANDSCAPE INFORMATION	It is drought tolerant and relatively fast growing. It has beautiful foliage.
PROPAGATION	Clean and soak seeds for 12 hours, then sow in beds or trays.
USES	The leaves are a rich source of medicinal compounds.

GT   21–30 days
GR   Medium

Grewia hirsuta | MALVACEAE

NAMES   Kukurbicha (C)/ Kalunnu (T)/ Kakarundah (H)

LEAF	**FLOWER**	**FRUIT**
STYLE Simple	**COLOUR** White/Cream	**COLOUR** Red
ARRANGEMENT Alternate	**AROMA** No	**SIZE** Less than 1 cm
THORN Absent	**SIZE** 1 to 3 cm	**TYPE** Drupe
LENGTH More than 5 cm		
WIDTH 1.5 to 5 cm		

DESCRIPTION   A deciduous shrub, with smooth bark and no thorns.

HABITAT   This shrub can be found in the open, or as a component of the understorey in a mature forest.

LANDSCAPE INFORMATION   It is drought tolerant, and is slow-growing.

PROPAGATION   Clean and soak seeds for 12 hours, then sow in beds or trays.

USES   The powdered root is mixed with water and applied as a dressing for wounds. There are also recorded uses in the treatment of heart disease, cough, diarrhoea and fever.

GT   1 month

GR   Medium

Ximenia americana | OLACACEAE

NAMES   Hog plum (c)/ Siru yelandhai (т)

LEAF	
STYLE	Simple
ARRANGEMENT	Alternate
THORN	Straight
LENGTH	1 to 3 cm
WIDTH	1.5 to 5 cm

FLOWER	
COLOUR	White/Cream
AROMA	Yes
SIZE	1 to 3 cm

FRUIT	
COLOUR	Orange
SIZE	1 to 3 cm
TYPE	Drupe

DESCRIPTION   A deciduous shrub, with smooth bark and thorns.

HABITAT   A shrub found mainly in disturbed areas, it grows in the full sun, disappearing if the canopy closes.

LANDSCAPE INFORMATION   The fruit has an attractive colour, and it can be grown as a hedge.

PROPAGATION   Clean seeds and soak for 24 hours, then sow in beds or trays.

GT   30 days
GR   Medium

USES   The fruit is edible, either raw or as a pickle, and the oil from the seed is used as a substitute for ghee. The wood can be used as a substitute for sandalwood in carpentry.

Flueggea leucopyrus | PHYLLANTHACEAE

NAMES   Bushweed (c)/ Vellaippoola (т)/ Shinar (н)

LEAF
STYLE Simple
ARRANGEMENT Alternate
THORN Straight
LENGTH 3 to 5 cm
WIDTH 1.5 to 5 cm

FLOWER
COLOUR White/Cream
AROMA Yes
SIZE Less than 1 cm

FRUIT
COLOUR White
SIZE Less than 1 cm
TYPE Berry

DESCRIPTION	A deciduous shrub, with smooth bark and thorns.
HABITAT	A shrub found mainly in disturbed areas, it grows in the full sun, disappearing if the canopy closes.
LANDSCAPE INFORMATION	It is drought tolerant and attracts butterflies.
PROPAGATION	Clean and soak seeds for 12 hours, then sow in beds or trays.
USES	The powdered leaves have been used as a head bath, and as a treatment for headaches.

GT 10–14 days
GR High

Flacourtia indica | SALICACEAE

NAMES   Governor's plum (c)/ Sothaikkala (t)/ Bilangada (h)

LEAF		FLOWER		FRUIT	
STYLE Simple		**COLOUR** White/Cream		**COLOUR** Red	
ARRANGEMENT Alternate		**AROMA** Yes		**SIZE** Less than 1 cm	
THORN Straight		**SIZE** Less than 1 cm		**TYPE** Drupe	
LENGTH 3 to 5 cm					
WIDTH 0.5 to 1.5 cm					

DESCRIPTION   A deciduous shrub, with smooth bark and thorns.

HABITAT   This shrub can be found in the open, or as a component of the understorey in a mature forest.

LANDSCAPE INFORMATION   It is drought tolerant and attracts butterflies.

PROPAGATION   Clean and soak seeds for 12 hours, then sow in beds or trays.

GT   1 month
GR   High

USES   The fruits are edible, and are suitable for jams, jellies and syrups.

Hildegardia populifolia | MALVACEAE

NAMES Poplar leaved ardor (c)/ Malaippuvarasu (T)

LEAF		FLOWER		FRUIT	
STYLE Simple		**COLOUR** Red		**COLOUR** Brown/Rusty	
ARRANGEMENT Alternate		**AROMA** Yes		**SIZE** More than 5 cm	
THORN Absent		**SIZE** 1 to 3 cm		**TYPE** Seedpod	
LENGTH More than 5 cm					
WIDTH More than 5 cm					

DESCRIPTION	A medium sized deciduous tree growing up to a height of 10 metres, with smooth bark and no thorns.
HABITAT	This tree enjoys the full sun. It is a component of the deciduous forest type and is found on hillocks.
LANDSCAPE INFORMATION	This is an interesting tree to include in a landscape as it has unique characteristics. Listed as critically endangered on the IUCN Red List.
PROPAGATION	Clean and soak seeds for 12 hours, then sow directly in bags or beds
USES	This plant may be a potential source of antioxidants, and the wood is used for making combs.

GT 10–14 days

GR High

Falconeria insignis | EUPHORBIACEAE

NAMES Chinese tallow (c)/ Sarkarai kalli (T)/ Khinna (H)

LEAF		FLOWER		FRUIT	
STYLE Simple		**COLOUR** Green		**COLOUR** Brown/Rusty	
ARRANGEMENT Alternate		**AROMA** No		**SIZE** Less than 1 cm	
THORN Absent		**SIZE** Less than 1 cm		**TYPE** Capsule	
LENGTH More than 5 cm					
WIDTH More than 5 cm					

DESCRIPTION	A medium sized deciduous tree growing up to a height of 10 metres, with rough bark and no thorns. Also known as *Sapium insigne*.
HABITAT	This tree enjoys the full sun. It is a component of the deciduous forest type, and is sometimes found in evergreen forest areas.
LANDSCAPE INFORMATION	It is a slow-growing and beautiful tree.
PROPAGATION	Soak seeds overnight, then sow in trays with coconut fibre.
USES	The white latex extracted from the bark is applied to cure scabies and boils. The wood is good for fencing and fuel.

GT 2 weeks

GR Medium

Semecarpus anacardium | ANACARDIACEAE

NAMES Marking nut tree (C)/ Seran kottai (T)/ Bhilawan (H)

LEAF
STYLE Simple
ARRANGEMENT Alternate
THORN Absent
LENGTH More than 5 cm
WIDTH More than 5 cm

FLOWER
COLOUR Green
AROMA Yes
SIZE Less than 1 cm

FRUIT
COLOUR Black
SIZE More than 5 cm
TYPE Nut

DESCRIPTION A medium sized deciduous tree growing up to a height of 10 metres, with rough bark and no thorns.

HABITAT This tree enjoys the full sun. It is generally found in disturbed areas, but mature specimens can also be found in evergreen stands.

LANDSCAPE INFORMATION It is a good component in ecological landscaping.

PROPAGATION Clean and soak seeds for 12 hours, then sow in beds or trays. Use gloves when cleaning.

GT 6 months
GR Medium

USES The nut was used by washermen and women to mark cloth before washing.

Euphorbia antiquorum | EUPHORBIACEAE

NAMES Triangular spurge (C)/ Sadurakkalli (T)/ Tridhara (H)

LEAF		FLOWER		FRUIT	
STYLE Simple		**COLOUR** Green		**COLOUR** Red	
ARRANGEMENT Alternate		**AROMA** No		**SIZE** Less than 1 cm	
THORN Straight		**SIZE** Less than 1 cm		**TYPE** Capsule	
LENGTH Less than 1 cm					
WIDTH Less than 1 cm					

DESCRIPTION A small deciduous tree growing up to a height of 6 metres, whose leaves are only present for a brief period, with rough bark and thorns found on young growth.

HABITAT This plant cannot tolerate shade, and enjoys the full sun. It is often found on hillocks.

LANDSCAPE INFORMATION This small tree attracts bees, and is good as a feature in the garden.

PROPAGATION Clean and soak seeds for 12 hours, then sow directly in bags or beds. Can propagate from cuttings.

USES The juice from the plant has been used to treat dropsy, and to kill maggots in wounds.

GT 1–2 months
GR Medium

Euphorbia nivulia | ANACARDIACEAE

NAMES   Leafy milk hedge (C)/ Ilai kalli (T)/ Katathohar (H)

<table>
<tr><td>LEAF</td><td>STYLE Simple
ARRANGEMENT Alternate
THORN Straight
LENGTH More than 5 cm
WIDTH 1.5 to 5 cm</td><td>FLOWER</td><td>COLOUR Green
AROMA No
SIZE Less than 1 cm</td><td>FRUIT</td><td>COLOUR Brown/Rusty
SIZE Less than 1 cm
TYPE Capsule</td></tr>
</table>

DESCRIPTION   A small deciduous tree growing up to a height of 6 metres, with rough bark and thorns found on young growth.

HABITAT   This plant cannot tolerate shade, and enjoys the full sun. It is often found on hillocks.

LANDSCAPE INFORMATION   It is slow-growing and has a beautiful form.

PROPAGATION   Clean and soak seeds for 12 hours, then sow directly in bags or beds. Can propagate from cuttings.

USES   This plant is used in Ayurvedic medicine for bronchitis, asthma, leprosy and jaundice.

GT   1–2 months
GR   Medium

Euphorbia tortilis | EUPHORBIACEAE

NAMES   Spiral cactus (C)/ Thirugukkalli (T)

LEAF
STYLE Simple
ARRANGEMENT Alternate
THORN Straight
LENGTH Absent
WIDTH Absent

FLOWER
COLOUR Yellow
AROMA No
SIZE Less than 1 cm

FRUIT
COLOUR Brown/Rusty
SIZE Less than 1 cm
TYPE Capsule

DESCRIPTION	A leafless shrub, with smooth stem and thorns.
HABITAT	This shrub is occasionally found in the forest areas, however it is more usually found by the side of the road, on tank bunds, or in agricultural boundaries.
LANDSCAPE INFORMATION	This tree attracts bees and is useful for fencing.
PROPAGATION	Clean and soak seeds overnight, sow in beds. Can propagate from cuttings.
USES	The whole plant is a traditional medicine for ulcers. The white sap is applied on the wounds of cattle to remove worms.

GT   1–2 months

GR   Medium

Bridelia retusa | PHYLLANTHACEAE

NAMES   Spinous kino tree (c)/ Mul vengai (T)/ Kaji (H)

LEAF
STYLE Simple
ARRANGEMENT Alternate
THORN Straight
LENGTH More than 5 cm
WIDTH 1.5 to 5 cm

FLOWER
COLOUR Green
AROMA No
SIZE Less than 1 cm

FRUIT
COLOUR Black
SIZE Less than 1 cm
TYPE Drupe

DESCRIPTION   A small deciduous tree growing up to a height of 6 metres, with rough bark and thorns.

HABITAT   This tree enjoys the full sun. It is generally found on hillocks, and occasionally on the plains on red soil.

LANDSCAPE INFORMATION   It is fast growing, and is good for creating an early canopy.

PROPAGATION   Clean and soak seeds for 12 hours, then sow in beds or trays.

USES   The bark mixed with sesame oil is used as a liniment for rheumatism and lumbago.

GT   2 weeks
GR   High

Cleistanthus collinus | PHYLLANTHACEAE

NAMES   Oduvan (T)/ Garari (H)

LEAF		FLOWER		FRUIT	
STYLE	Simple	**COLOUR**	Green	**COLOUR**	Brown/Rusty
ARRANGEMENT	Alternate	**AROMA**	Yes	**SIZE**	3 to 5 cm
THORN	Absent	**SIZE**	1 to 3 cm	**TYPE**	Capsule
LENGTH	3 to 5 cm				
WIDTH	1.5 to 5 cm				

DESCRIPTION	A small deciduous tree growing up to a height of 6 metres, with rough bark and no thorns.	
HABITAT	This tree enjoys the full sun. It is found on hillocks, and occasionally on the plains. It is rarely found in mature evergreen stands.	
LANDSCAPE INFORMATION	It is a good component in ecological landscaping. Listed as vulnerable on the IUCN Red List.	
PROPAGATION	Let fruits open in seed, soak seeds for 12 hours, then sow in beds.	GT 1 month
USES	This plant is poisonous and should not be ingested.	GR Medium

Ziziphus jujuba | RHAMNACEAE

NAMES Indian jujube (c)/ Ilandhai (t)/ Ber (h)

LEAF	STYLE Simple	**FLOWER**	COLOUR Green	**FRUIT**	COLOUR Red
	ARRANGEMENT Alternate		AROMA Yes		SIZE 2 to 3 cm
	THORN Recurved		SIZE Less than 1 cm		TYPE Drupe
	LENGTH 3 to 5 cm				
	WIDTH 1.5 to 5 cm				

DESCRIPTION — A medium sized deciduous tree growing up to a height of 10 metres, with rough bark and thorns found on young growth. Also known as *Ziziphus mauritiana*.

HABITAT — This plant is occasionally found in forest areas, however it is more usually found by the side of the road, on tank bunds, or in agricultural boundaries.

LANDSCAPE INFORMATION — It attracts bees, is drought tolerant, and in the right conditions will maintain an evergreen foliage.

PROPAGATION — Clean seeds and soak for 12 hours, then sow in beds or trays.

USES — The fruit is eaten raw or pickled. The wood is used for making rafters.

GT 1–2 months

GR High

Ziziphus xylopyrus | RHAMNACEAE

NAMES Woody fruit jujube (C)/ Kottai ilandhai (T)/ Kath ber (H)

LEAF
STYLE Simple
ARRANGEMENT Alternate
THORN Recurved
LENGTH More than 5 cm
WIDTH 1.5 to 5 cm

FLOWER
COLOUR Green
AROMA Yes
SIZE Less than 1 cm

FRUIT
COLOUR Grey
SIZE More than 5 cm
TYPE Drupe

DESCRIPTION	A small deciduous tree growing up to a height of 6 metres, with smooth bark and thorns found on young growth.
HABITAT	This plant is generally found in disturbed areas, and rarely found in mature evergreen stands.
LANDSCAPE INFORMATION	It is a good component in biodiversity landscaping.
PROPAGATION	Clean seeds and soak for 12 hours, then sow in beds or trays.
USES	The fruits are edible, and it is reported to treat diabetes and digestive and urinary disorders. The wood is used for charcoal and fuel.

GT 1 month
GR Medium

Casearia tomentosa | SALICACEAE

NAMES   Toothed leaf chilla (C)/ Naai azhinjil (T)/ Chilla (H)

LEAF		FLOWER		FRUIT	
STYLE	Simple	COLOUR	Green	COLOUR	Green
ARRANGEMENT	Alternate	AROMA	No	SIZE	1 to 3 cm
THORN	Absent	SIZE	Less than 1 cm	TYPE	Capsule
LENGTH	More than 5 cm				
WIDTH	1.5 to 5 cm				

DESCRIPTION   A small deciduous tree growing up to a height of 6 metres, with smooth bark and no thorns.

HABITAT   This tree enjoys the full sun. It is generally found in disturbed areas, and it is rarely found in mature evergreen stands.

LANDSCAPE INFORMATION   This tree can be used for variety in a landscape.

PROPAGATION   Clean seeds and soak for 12 hours, then sow in trays.

GT   2 weeks
GR   High

USES   The fruit can be used as a fish poison. The bark has been used as an external treatment for dropsy. The wood is good for making combs.

Antidesma ghaesembilla | PHYLLANTHACEAE

NAMES   Black currant tree (c)/ Pulicha maram (т)/ Januprulisaru (н)

LEAF		FLOWER		FRUIT	
STYLE Simple		**COLOUR** Green		**COLOUR** Purple/Blue	
ARRANGEMENT Alternate		**AROMA** No		**SIZE** Less than 1 cm	
THORN Absent		**SIZE** Less than 1 cm		**TYPE** Drupe	
LENGTH 3 to 5 cm					
WIDTH 1.5 to 5 cm					

DESCRIPTION   A small deciduous tree growing up to a height of 6 metres, with smooth bark and no thorns.

HABITAT   This tree enjoys the full sun. It is found in disturbed areas, and rarely found in mature evergreen stands.

LANDSCAPE INFORMATION   It attracts birds and is drought tolerant.

PROPAGATION   Clean and soak seeds for 12 hours, then sow in beds. Likes full sun to grow once established.

USES   The fruit is used as a purgative, while the bark has been used as an astringent and as a tonic.

GT 60–90 days

GR Medium

Breynia retusa | PHYLLANTHACEAE

NAMES   Cup saucer plant (c)/ Manippullandhi (t)/ Bahupraja (h)

LEAF
STYLE Simple
ARRANGEMENT Alternate
THORN Absent
LENGTH 1 to 3 cm
WIDTH 0.5 to 1.5 cm

FLOWER
COLOUR Green
AROMA No
SIZE Less than 1 cm

FRUIT
COLOUR Red
SIZE Less than 1 cm
TYPE Capsule

DESCRIPTION	A deciduous shrub, with smooth bark and no thorns.
HABITAT	A shrub found mainly in disturbed areas, it grows in the full sun, disappearing if the canopy closes.
LANDSCAPE INFORMATION	It is drought tolerant and attracts butterflies.
PROPAGATION	Clean and soak seeds for 12 hours, then sow in beds or trays.
USES	The bark is made into a paste and used as a liniment for rheumatism.

GT   1–2 months
GR   Medium

Breynia vitis-idaea | PHYLLANTHACEAE

NAMES   Mountain coffee bush (c)/ Seppula (T)/ Surasaruni (H)

LEAF	
STYLE Simple	
ARRANGEMENT Alternate	
THORN Absent	
LENGTH 3 to 5 cm	
WIDTH 1.5 to 5 cm	

FLOWER
COLOUR Yellow to green
AROMA No
SIZE Less than 1 cm

FRUIT
COLOUR Purple/Blue
SIZE 1 to 3 cm
TYPE Capsule

DESCRIPTION   A deciduous shrub, with smooth stem and no thorns.

HABITAT   This shrub can be found in the open, or as a component of the understorey in a mature forest. Also found along river banks.

LANDSCAPE INFORMATION   It is drought tolerant and attracts butterflies.

PROPAGATION   Clean and soak seeds for 12 hours, then sow in beds or trays.

GT   1–2 months
GR   Medium

USES   A decoction made from the roots has been given for snakebites, and the bark has been used to prevent haemorrhage.

Dodonaea viscosa | SAPINDACEAE

NAMES Hop bush (c)/ Viraali (T)/ Sanatta (H)/ Psychic awakening in matter (M)

LEAF	**STYLE** Simple		**FLOWER**	**COLOUR** Green	**FRUIT**	**COLOUR** Brown/Rusty
	ARRANGEMENT Alternate			**AROMA** No		**SIZE** 1 to 3 cm
	THORN Absent			**SIZE** Less than 1 cm		**TYPE** Capsule
	LENGTH More than 5 cm					
	WIDTH 1.5 to 5 cm					

DESCRIPTION A deciduous shrub, with rough bark and no thorns.

HABITAT A shrub found mainly in disturbed areas, it grows in full sun, and disappears if the canopy closes.

LANDSCAPE INFORMATION It is drought tolerant, has beautiful foliage, and is relatively fast growing.

PROPAGATION Clean and soak seeds for 12 hours, then sow directly in bags or beds. Best to use fresh seeds.

USES The leaf paste can be applied on cuts and wounds. The wood is extremely tough and durable, and can be used for fencing or firewood.

GT 30 days

GR Low

Cadaba fruticosa | CAPPARACEAE

NAMES Indian cadaba (c)/ Vizhudhi (T)/ Dabi (H)

LEAF	
STYLE	Simple
ARRANGEMENT	Alternate
THORN	Absent
LENGTH	3 to 5 cm
WIDTH	1.5 to 5 cm

FLOWER	
COLOUR	Yellow
AROMA	Yes
SIZE	1 to 3 cm

FRUIT	
COLOUR	Red
SIZE	3 to 5 cm
TYPE	Berry

DESCRIPTION	A deciduous shrub, with smooth bark and no thorns.
HABITAT	A shrub found mainly in disturbed areas, it grows in the full sun, becoming a straggler once the canopy closes.
LANDSCAPE INFORMATION	It is drought tolerant and attracts butterflies.
PROPAGATION	Clean and soak seeds for 12 hours, then sow in beds. Likes sun after transplanting. Can be done by cuttings.
USES	The leaves are reported as a traditional medicine for eczema, intestinal worms, and body pain, while the bark can be used as a nerve tonic.

GT 30–60 days
GR Medium

Grewia flavescens | MALVACEAE

NAMES Donkey berry (C)/ Sembarandai (T)

LEAF
- **STYLE** Simple
- **ARRANGEMENT** Alternate
- **THORN** Absent
- **LENGTH** More than 5 cm
- **WIDTH** 1.5 to 5 cm

FLOWER
- **COLOUR** Yellow
- **AROMA** Yes
- **SIZE** 1 to 3 cm

FRUIT
- **COLOUR** Brown/Rusty
- **SIZE** Less than 1 cm
- **TYPE** Drupe

DESCRIPTION A deciduous shrub, with smooth bark and no thorns.

HABITAT This shrub enjoys the full sun, it is found in disturbed areas, and is rarely found in mature evergreen stands. It is also found along riverbanks.

LANDSCAPE INFORMATION It has beautiful flowers, attracts birds, is fast growing, and is good for creating an early canopy.

PROPAGATION Clean and soak seeds for 12 hours, then sow in beds or trays.

USES The fruit is edible, and the roots have been used to treat menstrual problems. The branches are used for making baskets.

GT   1 month

GR   Medium

Grewia tiliifolia | MALVACEAE

NAMES   Common indian linden (c)/ Uunu (T)/ Dhamani (H)

LEAF
STYLE Simple
ARRANGEMENT Alternate
THORN Absent
LENGTH More than 5 cm
WIDTH More than 5 cm

FLOWER
COLOUR Yellow
AROMA Yes
SIZE 1 to 3 cm

FRUIT
COLOUR Red
SIZE Less than 1 cm
TYPE Drupe

DESCRIPTION	A small deciduous tree growing up to a height of 6 metres, with smooth bark and no thorns.
HABITAT	This tree enjoys the full sun. It is a component of the deciduous forest type, and is often found on the hillocks.
LANDSCAPE INFORMATION	This tree attracts birds. It is slow-growing and drought tolerant.
PROPAGATION	Clean and soak seeds overnight, then sow in trays.
USES	The fruits are edible, are good fodder, and have medicinal properties. The fibre from the inner bark is used to make cordage.

GT   1 month

GR   Medium

Ochna obtusata | OCHNACEAE

NAMES   Mickey Mouse bush (C)/ Silandi (T)/ Ramdhan champa (H)/
Greed for money (M)

LEAF	**STYLE** Simple	**FLOWER**	**COLOUR** Yellow	**FRUIT**	**COLOUR** Black
	ARRANGEMENT Alternate		**AROMA** No		**SIZE** Less than 1 cm
	THORN Absent		**SIZE** 3 to 5 cm		**TYPE** Drupe
	LENGTH More than 5 cm				
	WIDTH 1.5 to 5 cm				

DESCRIPTION   A deciduous shrub, with smooth bark and no thorns.

HABITAT   This shrub is found in the open, or as a component of the understorey in a mature forest.

LANDSCAPE INFORMATION   It is drought tolerant and attracts butterflies.

PROPAGATION   Clean and soak seeds for 24 hours, then sow in beds or trays.

GT   10–14 days

GR   High

USES   A decoction made from the bark has been used for dysentery, and the stem bark as a paste is applied on boils.

Helicteres isora | MALVACEAE

NAMES   East Indian screw tree (c)/ Valampuri (T)/ Marorphali (H)

LEAF		FLOWER		FRUIT	
STYLE	Simple	COLOUR	Orange	COLOUR	Brown/Rusty
ARRANGEMENT	Alternate	AROMA	Yes	SIZE	More than 5 cm
THORN	Absent	SIZE	1 to 3 cm	TYPE	Seedpod
LENGTH	More than 5 cm				
WIDTH	More than 5 cm				

DESCRIPTION   A deciduous shrub, with smooth bark and no thorns.

HABITAT   This shrub enjoys the full sun. It is generally found in disturbed areas, and is rarely found in mature forest stands.

LANDSCAPE INFORMATION   It has beautiful flowers, attracts butterflies, is fast growing, and good for creating an early canopy.

PROPAGATION   Clean and soak seeds for 12 hours, then sow in beds or trays.

USES   A decoction made from the bark has been used for treating diarrhoea and dysentery.

GT   60–90 days
GR   Very Low

Cordia monoica | BORAGINACEAE

NAMES Pasakkaimaram (T)

LEAF
STYLE Simple
ARRANGEMENT Alternate
THORN Absent
LENGTH More than 5 cm
WIDTH 1.5 to 5 cm

FLOWER
COLOUR White
AROMA Yes
SIZE Less than 1 cm

FRUIT
COLOUR Yellow
SIZE Less than 1 cm
TYPE Drupe

DESCRIPTION A small deciduous tree growing up to a height of 6 metres, with smooth bark and no thorns.

HABITAT This plant enjoys the full sun. It is generally found on the hillocks, or in mixed forest stands.

LANDSCAPE INFORMATION It is slow-growing and drought tolerant.

PROPAGATION Clean seeds and soak for 12 hours, then sow in beds.

USES A decoction made from the bark has been used as a treatment for dropsy.

GT 1 month
GR Medium

Cordia obliqua | BORAGINACEAE

NAMES   Indian cherry (c)/ Naru valli (T)/ Risalla (H)

LEAF
- **STYLE** Simple
- **ARRANGEMENT** Alternate
- **THORN** Absent
- **LENGTH** More than 5 cm
- **WIDTH** 1.5 to 5 cm

FLOWER
- **COLOUR** White/Cream
- **AROMA** No
- **SIZE** 1 to 3 cm

FRUIT
- **COLOUR** Pink
- **SIZE** 1 to 3 cm
- **TYPE** Drupe

DESCRIPTION	A medium sized deciduous tree growing up to a height of 10 metres, with rough bark and no thorns. Also known as *Cordia myxa*.
HABITAT	This tree is occasionally found in the forest areas, but is more usually found by the side of the road, on tank bunds, or in agricultural boundaries.
LANDSCAPE INFORMATION	This tree attracts birds. It is fast growing and drought tolerant. It is a good species for afforestation programmes.
PROPAGATION	Clean and soak seeds overnight, sow in beds.
USES	All parts of the tree are edible. A paste made from the leaves can relieve ulcers and headaches. The fruit is useful to treat coughs.

GT   2 weeks

GR   High

Salacia chinensis | CELASTRACEAE

NAMES Chinese salacia (T)/ Pon korandi (T)

LEAF
- **STYLE** Simple
- **ARRANGEMENT** Opposite
- **THORN** Absent
- **LENGTH** More than 5 cm
- **WIDTH** 1.5 to 5 cm

FLOWER
- **COLOUR** Green
- **AROMA** Yes
- **SIZE** Less than 1 cm

FRUIT
- **COLOUR** Red
- **SIZE** Less than 1 cm
- **TYPE** Berry

DESCRIPTION	An evergreen straggler, with smooth bark and no thorns.
HABITAT	This plant will stand alone as a shrub in disturbed areas, or it will grow up into the canopy.
LANDSCAPE INFORMATION	It is drought tolerant, has beautiful foliage, and is relatively fast growing.
PROPAGATION	Clean and soak seeds for 12 hours, then sow in beds or trays.
USES	The root bark has been used for treating gonorrhoea and rheumatism, as well as stimulating circulation.

GT 30 days
GR High

Gyrocarpus americanus | HERNANDIACEAE

NAMES Helicopter tree (c)/ Vellai thanakku (T)

LEAF
STYLE Simple to lobed
ARRANGEMENT Spiral
THORN Absent
LENGTH More than 5 cm
WIDTH More than 5 cm

FLOWER
COLOUR White
AROMA Yes
SIZE Less than 1 cm

FRUIT
COLOUR Brown/Rusty
SIZE 3 to 5 cm
TYPE Drupe

DESCRIPTION	A medium sized deciduous tree growing up to a height of 10 metres, with smooth bark and no thorns.
HABITAT	This tree enjoys the full sun, and it is generally found in exposed locations on the hillocks.
LANDSCAPE INFORMATION	This is an interesting tree to include in a landscape as it has unique characteristics.
PROPAGATION	Clean and soak seeds for 12 hours, then sow in beds or trays.
USES	The wood is used for making toys, light furniture, boxes, trays and floats. It has traditionally been used for dug-out canoes.

GT 30 days
GR Medium

Bauhinia racemosa | FABACEAE

NAMES   Bidi leaf tree (c)/ Aathi (t)/ Katmauli (h)

LEAF		FLOWER		FRUIT	
STYLE Lobed		**COLOUR** White/Cream		**COLOUR** Brown/Rusty	
ARRANGEMENT Alternate		**AROMA** No		**SIZE** More than 5 cm	
THORN Absent		**SIZE** 1 to 3 cm		**TYPE** Seedpod	
LENGTH 3 to 5 cm					
WIDTH 1.5 to 5 cm					

DESCRIPTION   A medium sized deciduous tree growing up to a height of 10 metres, with rough bark and no thorns.

HABITAT   Mature specimens are more often found in forest remnants that are less disturbed, however it can also be found in degraded areas in a modified form.

LANDSCAPE INFORMATION   It is drought tolerant, has beautiful foliage, and is relatively fast growing.

PROPAGATION   Clean seeds, scratch and soak for 12 hours, then sow directly in bags.

USES   This plant has been used as a treatment for bacterial and fungal infections, asthma and diabetes. The leaves are used for making bidi.

GT   10 days
GR   High

Bauhinia tomentosa | FABACEAE

NAMES   Yellow bauhinia (c)/ Iruvaatchi (т)/ Kachnal (н)/ Gold (м)

LEAF
STYLE Lobed
ARRANGEMENT Alternate
THORN Absent
LENGTH 3 to 5 cm
WIDTH 1.5 to 5 cm

FLOWER
COLOUR Yellow
AROMA Yes
SIZE More than 5 cm

FRUIT
COLOUR Brown/Rusty
SIZE More than 5 cm
TYPE Seedpod

DESCRIPTION   A shrub or small deciduous tree growing up to a height of 6 metres, with rough bark and no thorns.

HABITAT   This shrub is found mainly in disturbed areas. It grows in full sun, disappearing if the canopy closes.

LANDSCAPE INFORMATION   It has beautiful flowers, is fast growing, and is good for creating an early canopy.

PROPAGATION   Clean seeds, scratch and soak for 12 hours, then sow directly in bags.

GT   30–60 days
GR   High

USES   The leaves are used to make pickles. The buds and flowers have been used to treat dysentery, and the bark has been used for skin problems.

Sterculia urens | MALVACEAE

NAMES   Gum karaya (c)/ Senthanukku (t)/ Kulu (h)

LEAF
STYLE Lobed
ARRANGEMENT Alternate
THORN Absent
LENGTH More than 5 cm
WIDTH More than 5 cm

FLOWER
COLOUR Green
AROMA Yes
SIZE Less than 1 cm

FRUIT
COLOUR Brown/Rusty
SIZE More than 5 cm
TYPE Capsule

DESCRIPTION | A medium sized deciduous tree growing up to a height of 10 metres, with smooth bark and no thorns. Also known as *Firmiana simplex*.

HABITAT | This plant enjoys the full sun. It is found on hillocks in exposed locations.

LANDSCAPE INFORMATION | It is a beautiful, slow-growing tree.

PROPAGATION | Clean and soak seeds for 12 hours, then sow in beds or trays. Use gloves when cleaning.

USES | The roasted seeds are edible and are called java olives.

GT   30 days
GR   Medium

Cochlospermum religiosum | BIXACEAE

NAMES Yellow silk cotton (c)/ Kongilavam (t)/ Galgal (h)/
Success in supramental work (m)

LEAF	STYLE Lobed		**FLOWER**	COLOUR Yellow		**FRUIT**	COLOUR Brown/Rusty
	ARRANGEMENT Alternate			AROMA No			SIZE More than 5 cm
	THORN Absent			SIZE More than 5 cm			TYPE Capsule
	LENGTH More than 5 cm						
	WIDTH More than 5 cm						

DESCRIPTION	A medium sized deciduous tree growing up to a height of 10 metres, with rough bark and no thorns.
HABITAT	This tree enjoys the full sun, and it is found on exposed hillocks.
LANDSCAPE INFORMATION	This is an interesting tree to include in a landscape as it has beautiful yellow flowers and unique characteristics.
PROPAGATION	Clean seeds and soak for 12 hours, then sow in beds. Don't overwater until first leaves appear. Seedling aftercare required.
USES	The gum is sweetish. The wood has timber value, and the fibre is used for pillows.

GT	30 days
GR	Medium

Givotia moluccana | EUPHORBIACEAE

NAMES White catamaran tree (C)/ Kottai thanakku (T)

LEAF
STYLE Lobed
ARRANGEMENT Alternate
THORN Absent
LENGTH More than 5 cm
WIDTH More than 5 cm

FLOWER
COLOUR Yellow
AROMA No
SIZE Less than 1 cm

FRUIT
COLOUR Grey
SIZE 3 to 5 cm
TYPE Drupe

DESCRIPTION A large, spreading deciduous tree growing over 10 metres in height, with rough bark and no thorns.

HABITAT This tree enjoys the full sun. It is found on hillocks, either in exposed locations, or as a part of a mixed forest stand.

LANDSCAPE INFORMATION It is drought tolerant, has beautiful foliage, and is relatively fast growing.

PROPAGATION Crack and soak seeds for 12 hours, then sow directly in bags or beds.

GT 30 days
GR Medium

USES The leaf extract has been used as a remedy for liver ailments. The seed oil is used as a lubricant for fine machinery.

Firmiana colorata | MALVACEAE

NAMES Scarlet sterculia (C)/ Malapparuthi (T)/ Bodula(H)

LEAF		FLOWER		FRUIT	
STYLE Lobed		**COLOUR** Orange		**COLOUR** Brown/Rusty	
ARRANGEMENT Alternate		**AROMA** Yes		**SIZE** 3 to 5 cm	
THORN Absent		**SIZE** Less than 1 cm		**TYPE** Seedpod	
LENGTH More than 5 cm					
WIDTH More than 5 cm					

DESCRIPTION	A small deciduous tree growing up to a height of 6 metres, with smooth bark and no thorns.	
HABITAT	This tree enjoys the full sun. It is found on hillocks in exposed locations.	
LANDSCAPE INFORMATION	It is drought tolerant, has beautiful foliage, and is relatively fast growing.	
PROPAGATION	Clean and soak seeds for 12 hours, then sow in beds or trays. High mortality rate post germination. Care after transplanting.	GT 30 days GR Medium
USES	The bark yields a fibre that can be used to make ropes. A bark decoction has been used as a treatment for urinary infections and stomach pain.	

Stereospermum tetragonum | BIGNONIACEAE

NAMES Trumpet flower (c)/ Pooppadiri (T)/ Patiri (H)

LEAF		**FLOWER**		**FRUIT**	
STYLE	Lobed	COLOUR	Green	COLOUR	Brown/Rusty
ARRANGEMENT	Alternate	AROMA	Yes	SIZE	More than 5 cm
THORN	Absent	SIZE	Less than 1 cm	TYPE	Capsule
LENGTH	More than 5 cm				
WIDTH	More than 5 cm				

DESCRIPTION
A tall brevideciduous tree growing over 10 metres in height, with rough bark and no thorns. Also known as *Stereospermum personatum*.

HABITAT
This tree enjoys the full sun. It is found on hillocks, and rarely on the plains in mature forest stands.

LANDSCAPE INFORMATION
It is drought tolerant, has beautiful foliage, attracts bees, and is relatively fast growing.

PROPAGATION
Clean and soak seeds for 12 hours, then sow in beds with a light soil covering. Don't overwater beds. Needs sun after transplanting.

GT 10–14 days

GR Medium

USES
The wood is used for making furniture.

Chukrasia tabularis | MELIACEAE

NAMES   Chittagong wood (C)/ Malai vembu (T)/ Chikrasi (H)

LEAF
STYLE Pinnate
ARRANGEMENT Alternate
THORN Absent
LENGTH More than 5 cm
WIDTH 1.5 to 5 cm

FLOWER
COLOUR White/Cream
AROMA Yes
SIZE 1 to 3 cm

FRUIT
COLOUR Brown/Rusty
SIZE More than 5 cm
TYPE Capsule

DESCRIPTION	A tall deciduous tree growing over 10 metres in height, with rough bark and no thorns.
HABITAT	This tree enjoys the full sun. It is a component of the deciduous forest type, and is generally found in the hills.
LANDSCAPE INFORMATION	This is a relatively fast growing tree. It is drought tolerant with beautiful foliage.
PROPAGATION	Soak seeds overnight, then sow directly in beds.
USES	It is planted in coffee plantations for shade, and it is a valuable timber tree. The bark is used to treat fever and diarrhoea.

GT   2 weeks
GR   Medium

Dolichandrone falcata | BIGNONIACEAE

NAMES Medhshingi (C)/ Kadalathi (T)/ Hawar (H)

LEAF
STYLE Pinnate
ARRANGEMENT Opposite
THORN Absent
LENGTH 3 to 5 cm
WIDTH 1.5 to 5 cm

FLOWER
COLOUR White/Cream
AROMA Yes
SIZE 1 to 3 cm

FRUIT
COLOUR Brown/Rusty
SIZE More than 5 cm
TYPE Capsule

DESCRIPTION A small deciduous tree growing up to a height of 6 metres, with smooth bark and no thorns.

HABITAT This tree enjoys the full sun. It is found in areas of disturbance, and rarely found in mature forest stands.

LANDSCAPE INFORMATION It is slow-growing and drought tolerant.

PROPAGATION Clean and soak seeds for 12 hours, then sow in beds with a light soil covering. Don't overwater beds. Requires sun once transplanted.

GT 10–14 days
GR Medium

USES A leaf paste applied externally has been used to treat headaches and swollen glands.

Fernandoa adenophylla | BIGNONIACEAE

NAMES   Karen wood (C)/ Marodphali (T)

LEAF		FLOWER		FRUIT	
STYLE Pinnate		**COLOUR** Yellow		**COLOUR** Brown/Rusty	
ARRANGEMENT Opposite		**AROMA** No		**SIZE** More than 5 cm	
THORN Absent		**SIZE** More than 5 cm		**TYPE** Capsule	
LENGTH 1.5 to 5 cm					
WIDTH 1.5 to 5 cm					

DESCRIPTION	A medium sized deciduous tree growing up to a height of 10 metres, with rough bark and no thorns. Also known as *Heterophragma adenophyllum*.
HABITAT	This tree enjoys the full sun. It is a component of the deciduous forest type. It is sometimes found on agricultural boundaries.
LANDSCAPE INFORMATION	It is a good component in ecological landscaping.
PROPAGATION	Soak seeds overnight, then sow in beds. Young seedlings are sensitive to overwatering, and need good light once transplanted.
USES	The wood is good timber. In traditional medicine, oil extracted from the bark is used for massage.

GT   5–10 days
GR   High

Lepisanthes tetraphylla | SAPINDACEAE

NAMES Gugamathi (T)/ Kurpa (H)

LEAF		FLOWER		FRUIT	
STYLE Pinnate		**COLOUR** White/Cream		**COLOUR** Yellow	
ARRANGEMENT Alternate		**AROMA** Yes		**SIZE** 1 to 3 cm	
THORN Absent		**SIZE** Less than 1 cm		**TYPE** Drupe	
LENGTH More than 5 cm					
WIDTH More than 5 cm					

DESCRIPTION A medium sized evergreen tree growing up to a height of 10 metres, with rough bark and no thorns.

HABITAT Mature specimens are often found in undisturbed forest remnants, however it can also be found in degraded areas in a modified form.

LANDSCAPE INFORMATION It is drought tolerant, has evergreen foliage, and is slow-growing.

PROPAGATION Clean and soak seeds for 12 hours, then sow directly in bags or beds. Very slow growth in nursery.

USES This tree is considered sacred, and the fruits are edible. The wood is used for furniture and carving.

GT 30–60 days

GR Medium

Schleichera oleosa | SAPINDACEAE

NAMES Ceylon oak (c)/ Kumbathiri (t)/ Kosam (h)

LEAF	
STYLE	Pinnate
ARRANGEMENT	Alternate
THORN	Absent
LENGTH	1.5 to 5 cm
WIDTH	1.5 to 5 cm

FLOWER	
COLOUR	White/Cream
AROMA	No
SIZE	Less than 1 cm

FRUIT	
COLOUR	Red
SIZE	1 to 3 cm
TYPE	Drupe

DESCRIPTION	A medium sized brevideciduous tree growing up to a height of 6 metres, with smooth bark and no thorns.
HABITAT	This tree is mainly found on the hillocks, and occasionally found on rocky slopes, or in more dense forest.
LANDSCAPE INFORMATION	With its beautiful foliage and form, this tree is nice in a large landscaped area.
PROPAGATION	Crack seeds and soak for 24 hours. Sow in beds.
USES	The fruits are edible. Kusum oil, extracted from the seeds, is used for hairdressing, culinary and lighting purposes. In traditional medicine, it is applied to cure skin afflictions.

GT 10–14 days

GR Medium

Glycosmis mauritiana | RUTACEAE

NAMES   Orange berry (c)/ Konji (T)/ Ban neem (H)

LEAF	**STYLE** Pinnate	
	ARRANGEMENT Alternate	
	THORN Absent	
	LENGTH More than 5 cm	
	WIDTH 1.5 to 5 cm	

FLOWER
COLOUR White/Cream
AROMA Yes
SIZE Less than 1 cm

FRUIT
COLOUR Pink
SIZE Less than 1 cm
TYPE Berry

DESCRIPTION	An evergreen shrub, with smooth bark and no thorns.
HABITAT	This shrub is normally found in the understorey of the forest, and only if the canopy has been recently removed will it be found in the open sun.
LANDSCAPE INFORMATION	It is drought tolerant, has beautiful foliage, and is relatively fast growing.
PROPAGATION	Clean and soak seeds for 12 hours, then sow in beds or trays.
USES	The fruits are edible, and the plant has been used to treat arthritis, urinary infections, cough, bronchitis, asthma and diarrhoea.

GT   10–14 days
GR   Very High

Murraya paniculata | RUTACEAE

NAMES Queen of the night (c)/ Vengarai (T)/ Kamini (H)/ Peace in the vital (M)

LEAF
STYLE Pinnate
ARRANGEMENT Alternate
THORN Absent
LENGTH 3 to 5 cm
WIDTH 1.5 to 5 cm

FLOWER
COLOUR White/Cream
AROMA Yes
SIZE 1 to 3 cm

FRUIT
COLOUR Red
SIZE Less than 1 cm
TYPE Berry

DESCRIPTION	An evergreen shrub, with rough bark and no thorns.
HABITAT	This shrub is normally found in the understorey of the forest, and only if the canopy has been recently removed will it be found in the open sun.
LANDSCAPE INFORMATION	It is drought tolerant, has beautiful foliage, is relatively fast growing, and can be planted as a hedge. This shrub attracts birds, butterflies and bees.
PROPAGATION	Clean and soak seeds for 12 hours, then sow in beds or trays.
USES	The root made into a paste has been used as a rub for body pain. The wood makes good tool handles.

GT 7–10 days
GR High

Aglaia elaeagnoidea | MELIACEAE

NAMES   Droopy leaf tree (c)/ Sokkala (t)/ Priyangu (h)/
Mental suggestion of organisation (m)

LEAF

STYLE Pinnate
ARRANGEMENT Alternate
THORN Absent
LENGTH More than 5 cm
WIDTH 1.5 to 5 cm

FLOWER

COLOUR Yellow
AROMA Yes
SIZE Less than 1 cm

FRUIT

COLOUR Orange
SIZE Less than 1 cm
TYPE Berry

DESCRIPTION   A medium sized evergreen tree growing up to a
height of 10 metres, with smooth bark and no thorns.

HABITAT   Mature specimens are often found in undisturbed
forest remnants, however it can also be found in
degraded areas in a modified form.

LANDSCAPE   It is drought tolerant, has beautiful foliage, and is
INFORMATION   relatively fast growing.

PROPAGATION   Clean and sow directly in bags or beds.

USES   The fruits have been used in the treatment of
inflammation and leprosy. The bright, hard red
wood is used for timber.

GT   30 days
GR   High

Azadirachta indica | MELIACEAE

NAMES Neem (C)/ Vembu (T)/ Spiritual atmosphere (M)

LEAF
STYLE Pinnate
ARRANGEMENT Alternate
THORN Absent
LENGTH More than 5 cm
WIDTH 1.5 to 5 cm

FLOWER
COLOUR White/Cream
AROMA Yes
SIZE Less than 1 cm

FRUIT
COLOUR Yellow
SIZE 1 to 3 cm
TYPE Drupe

DESCRIPTION	A medium sized deciduous tree growing up to a height of 10 metres, with rough bark and no thorns.
HABITAT	This tree is occasionally found in forest areas, however it is more usually found by the side of the road, on tank bunds, or in agricultural boundaries.
LANDSCAPE INFORMATION	It is drought tolerant, has beautiful foliage, and is relatively fast growing.
PROPAGATION	Clean and sow directly in bags.
USES	Neem has a long history of use in Ayurvedic and Siddha medicine, particularly for treating skin conditions. It is also a valuable timber tree.

GT 10 days

GR High

Boswellia serrata | BURSERACEAE

NAMES Indian frankincense (C)/ Kunkilium (T)/ Salai (H)

LEAF
STYLE Pinnate
ARRANGEMENT Alternate
THORN Absent
LENGTH 0.5 to 1.5 cm
WIDTH 0.5 to 1.5 cm

FLOWER
COLOUR White/Cream
AROMA No
SIZE Less than 1 cm

FRUIT
COLOUR Brown/Rusty
SIZE 1 to 3 cm
TYPE Drupe

DESCRIPTION	A tall deciduous tree growing over 10 metres in height, with rough bark and no thorns.
HABITAT	This tree is found on the hillocks, where it requires a well-drained soil and a good amount of light to flourish.
LANDSCAPE INFORMATION	With its beautiful foliage and flowers, this tree is good for park areas.
PROPAGATION	Soak seeds overnight, then sow in trays with coconut fibre. Young seedlings are sensitive to overwatering, and need good light once transplanted.
USES	Frankincense resin is used to make incense, and as a medicine for its anti-inflammatory properties.

GT 2 weeks
GR Medium

Pungan / Karanj
Pongamia pinnata

JACKAL MANGO / *Ambara*
Spondias pinnata

Commiphora caudata | BURSERACEAE

NAMES   Green commiphora (c)/ Pachai kiluvai (т)/ Ikkata (н)

LEAF		FLOWER		FRUIT	
STYLE Pinnate		**COLOUR** White/Cream		**COLOUR** Yellow	
ARRANGEMENT Alternate		**AROMA** Yes		**SIZE** 1 to 3 cm	
THORN Straight		**SIZE** Less than 1 cm		**TYPE** Drupe	
LENGTH 3 to 5 cm					
WIDTH 1.5 to 5 cm					

DESCRIPTION   A medium sized deciduous tree growing up to a height of 10 metres, with smooth bark and no thorns.

HABITAT   This tree enjoys the full sun. It is generally found in exposed locations on hillocks, and rarely found in mature evergreen stands.

LANDSCAPE INFORMATION   This small tree is good as a feature in the garden.

PROPAGATION   Clean seeds and soak for 12 hours, then sow in beds.

GT 1–2 months

GR Medium

USES   The leaf paste has been applied on cracked lips and foot corns. The gum mixed with water has been used to treat mouth ulcers, rheumatoid arthritis, and for wound healing.

Garuga pinnata | BURSERACEAE

NAMES   Karuvembu (T)/ Kharpat (H)

LEAF	**STYLE** Pinnate		**FLOWER**	**COLOUR** White/Cream	**FRUIT**	**COLOUR** Yellow
	ARRANGEMENT Alternate			**AROMA** No		**SIZE** 1 to 3 cm
	THORN Absent			**SIZE** Less than 1 cm		**TYPE** Drupe
	LENGTH 3 to 5 cm					
	WIDTH 1.5 to 5 cm					

DESCRIPTION
A medium sized deciduous tree growing up to a height of 10 metres, with smooth bark and no thorns.

HABITAT
This tree enjoys the full sun. It is generally found on hillocks in mixed forest areas.

LANDSCAPE INFORMATION
This tree is a good component in ecological landscaping.

PROPAGATION
Clean and soak seeds for 12 hours, then sow in beds or trays. High mortality rate post germination. Care needed after transplanting.

GT 30 days
GR Medium

USES
The raw fruits are edible and can be used to make pickles. The leaf juice mixed with honey has been used to treat asthma.

Soymida febrifuga | MELIACEAE

NAMES Indian redwood (c)/ Sem (T)/ Rohan (H)

LEAF		FLOWER		FRUIT	
STYLE	Pinnate	COLOUR	White/Cream	COLOUR	Brown/Rusty
ARRANGEMENT	Alternate	AROMA	No	SIZE	More than 5 cm
THORN	Absent	SIZE	1 to 3 cm	TYPE	Capsule
LENGTH	More than 5 cm				
WIDTH	1.5 to 5 cm				

DESCRIPTION	A medium sized deciduous tree growing up to a height of 10 metres, with rough bark and no thorns.
HABITAT	This tree enjoys the full sun. It is a component of the deciduous forest type, and is generally found on the lower slopes of the hills.
LANDSCAPE INFORMATION	It is a tree with beautiful foliage and form, and works well in a large landscaped area.
PROPAGATION	Soak seeds overnight, then sow in trays with coconut fibre. Young seedlings are sensitive to overwatering, and need good light once transplanted.
USES	The bark has been used as a febrifuge instead of quinine.

GT 2 weeks

GR Medium

Acacia chundra | FABACEAE

NAMES   Cutch tree (C)/ Karungali (T)/ Katha (H)

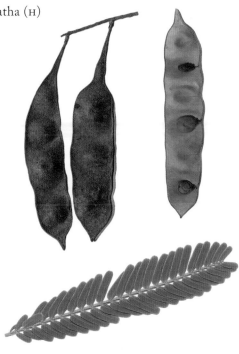

LEAF
STYLE Pinnate
ARRANGEMENT Alternate
THORN Straight to Recurved
LENGTH Less than 1 cm
WIDTH Less than 0.5 cm

FLOWER
COLOUR White/Cream
AROMA Yes
SIZE 1 to 3 cm

FRUIT
COLOUR Brown/Rusty
SIZE More than 5 cm
TYPE Seedpod

DESCRIPTION	A small deciduous tree growing up to a height of 6 metres, with rough bark and thorns found on young growth.
HABITAT	This tree enjoys the full sun. It is generally found in disturbed areas, and rarely found in mature evergreen stands.
LANDSCAPE INFORMATION	It is fast growing and is good for fencing.
PROPAGATION	Clean and soak seeds for 12 hours, then sow directly in bags or beds.
USES	The wood is used for making beams, posts and agricultural implements.

GT   5–10 days
GR   High

Acacia leucophloea | FABACEAE

NAMES White bark acacia (c)/ Vel velan (t)/ Reonja (h)/ Knowledge of details (m)

LEAF	**STYLE** Pinnate		**FLOWER**	**COLOUR** White/Cream		**FRUIT**	**COLOUR** Green
	ARRANGEMENT Alternate			**AROMA** Yes			**SIZE** More than 5 cm
	THORN Straight			**SIZE** Less than 1 cm			**TYPE** Seedpod
	LENGTH Less than 1 cm						
	WIDTH Less than 0.5 cm						

DESCRIPTION
A medium sized deciduous tree growing up to a height of 10 metres, with rough bark and thorns found on young growth. Also known as *Vachellia leucophloea*.

HABITAT
This tree enjoys the full sun. It is generally found in disturbed areas, and rarely found in mature evergreen stands.

LANDSCAPE INFORMATION
It is good as a live fence.

PROPAGATION
Clean and soak seeds for 12 hours, then sow directly in bags or beds.

GT 5–10 days
GR High

USES
The bark yields a fibre that is used for cordage and fishing nets. The wood is used for construction and is very suitable for making charcoal.

Acacia nilotica subsp. indica | FABACEAE

NAMES   Gum arabic (C)/ Karuvel (T)/ Babool (H)

LEAF		
STYLE Pinnate	**FLOWER**	**FRUIT**
ARRANGEMENT Alternate	COLOUR Yellow	COLOUR Grey
THORN Straight	AROMA Yes	SIZE More than 5 cm
LENGTH Less than 1 cm	SIZE 1 to 3 cm	TYPE Seedpod
WIDTH Less than 0.5 cm		

DESCRIPTION   A medium sized deciduous tree growing up to a height of 10 metres, with rough bark and thorns found on young growth. Also known as *Vachelia nilotica*

HABITAT   A naturalized exotic that is found mainly near water bodies. It has been planted in some forest areas and is also found growing wild in other locations.

LANDSCAPE INFORMATION   It is a good component in ecological landscaping.

GT   5–10 days

GR   High

PROPAGATION   Clean and soak seeds for 12 hours, then sow directly in bags or beds.

USES   The branchlets are used as a toothbrush, and a decoction of the fruit has been used to help with fever. The seeds have been used to treat malaria, diabetes and hypertension.

Acacia planifrons | FABACEAE

NAMES   Umbrella thorn (c)/ Kudai vel (t)

LEAF
STYLE Pinnate
ARRANGEMENT Alternate
THORN Straight
LENGTH 0.5 to 1.5 cm
WIDTH 0.5 to 1.5 cm

FLOWER
COLOUR White/Cream
AROMA No
SIZE 1 to 3 cm

FRUIT
COLOUR Brown/Rusty
SIZE More than 5 cm
TYPE Seedpod

DESCRIPTION	A small deciduous tree growing up to a height of 6 metres, with rough bark and thorns. Also known as *Vachellia planifrons*.
HABITAT	This tree is commonly planted on hillocks or wastelands. It is also a component of the dry deciduous forest type.
LANDSCAPE INFORMATION	This tree is iconic when mature. It is great for landscaping in large, hilly areas.
PROPAGATION	Clean and soak seeds for 6 hours, then sow in beds.
USES	The leaves and pods are fodder for goats, and the wood is an excellent fuel. The bark is used to treat wounds and other skin problems.

GT   5–10 days

GR   High

Albizia amara | FABACEAE

NAMES Oil cake tree (c)/ Usilai (T)/ Krishna siris (H)

LEAF
STYLE Pinnate
ARRANGEMENT Alternate
THORN Absent
LENGTH Less than 1 cm
WIDTH Less than 0.5 cm

FLOWER
COLOUR White/Cream
AROMA Yes
SIZE 1 to 3 cm

FRUIT
COLOUR Brown/Rusty
SIZE More than 5 cm
TYPE Seedpod

DESCRIPTION	A medium sized deciduous tree growing up to a height of 10 metres, with smooth bark and no thorns.
HABITAT	This tree enjoys the full sun, and it can be found in both disturbed and mature forest stands.
LANDSCAPE INFORMATION	It is drought tolerant, has beautiful foliage, and is relatively fast growing.
PROPAGATION	Clean and soak seeds for 12 hours, then sow directly in bags or beds.
USES	The bark has been used for tooth infections and relieving pain. The leaf paste can be applied for dandruff, lice, skin diseases and poisonous bites. The wood is used for construction.

GT 5–10 days
GR Very High

Albizia lathamii | FABACEAE

NAMES   Stipulate siris (c)

LEAF	STYLE Pinnate	**FLOWER**	COLOUR White/Cream	**FRUIT**	COLOUR Brown/Rusty
	ARRANGEMENT Alternate		AROMA No		SIZE More than 5 cm
	THORN Absent		SIZE 1 to 3 cm		TYPE Seedpod
	LENGTH 0.5 to 1.5 cm				
	WIDTH 0.5 to 1.5 cm				

DESCRIPTION	A medium sized deciduous tree growing up to a height of 10 metres, with rough bark and no thorns.
HABITAT	This rare tree is found in the southern districts, in temple groves or forest remnants.
LANDSCAPE INFORMATION	This tree is good to include in ecological landscaping as it is drought tolerant and attracts bees. Listed as critically endangered on the IUCN Red List.
PROPAGATION	Clean and soak seeds for 6 hours, then sow in beds.
USES	The wood is used for fuel, and the leaves and seedpods are used for fodder.

GT 5–10 days
GR High

Albizia lebbeck | FABACEAE

NAMES   Siris tree (C)/ Vaagai (T)/ Saras (H)/ Integral wisdom (M)

LEAF	**STYLE** Pinnate	**FLOWER**	**COLOUR** White/Cream	**FRUIT**	**COLOUR** Brown/Rusty
	ARRANGEMENT Alternate		**AROMA** Yes		**SIZE** More than 5 cm
	THORN Absent		**SIZE** 1 to 3 cm		**TYPE** Seedpod
	LENGTH Less than 1 cm				
	WIDTH Less than 0.5 cm				

DESCRIPTION   A large deciduous tree growing over 10 metres in height, with rough bark and no thorns.

HABITAT   This tree is occasionally found in forest areas, however it is more usually found by the side of the road, on tank bunds, or in agricultural boundaries.

LANDSCAPE INFORMATION   It has beautiful flowers, is fast growing, and is good for creating an early canopy.

PROPAGATION   Clean and soak seeds for 12 hours, then sow directly in bags or beds. Care required after transplanting seedlings.

USES   The wood is used as planks for carts.

GT   5–10 days

GR   High

Albizia odoratissima | FABACEAE

NAMES   Black siris (C)/ Karuvaagai (T)/ Kala siris (H)

LEAF
STYLE Pinnate
ARRANGEMENT Alternate
THORN Absent
LENGTH 15 to 20 cm
WIDTH More than 10 cm

FLOWER
COLOUR White/Cream
AROMA Yes
SIZE 1 to 3 cm

FRUIT
COLOUR Black
SIZE More than 5 cm
TYPE Seedpod

DESCRIPTION	A medium sized deciduous tree growing up to a height of 10 metres, with rough bark and no thorns.
HABITAT	This tree enjoys the full sun. It is generally found on hillocks, and rarely found in mature evergreen stands.
LANDSCAPE INFORMATION	It is fast growing, and is good for creating an early canopy.
PROPAGATION	Clean and soak seeds for 12 hours, then sow directly in bags or beds.
USES	The leaves have been used as a remedy for cough, the bark for ulcers and skin diseases.

GT   5–10 days
GR   High

Dalbergia lanceolaria subsp. paniculata | FABACEAE

NAMES   Erigai (T)/ Passi (H)

LEAF
STYLE Pinnate
ARRANGEMENT Alternate
THORN Absent
LENGTH 3 to 5 cm
WIDTH 1.5 to 5 cm

FLOWER
COLOUR White/Cream
AROMA Yes
SIZE 1 to 3 cm

FRUIT
COLOUR Brown/Rusty
SIZE More than 5 cm
TYPE Seedpod

DESCRIPTION   A medium sized deciduous tree growing up to a height of 10 metres, with smooth bark and no thorns.

HABITAT   This tree enjoys the full sun. It is generally found in disturbed areas, and rarely found in mature evergreen stands.

LANDSCAPE INFORMATION   It has beautiful flowers, is fast growing, and is good for creating an early canopy.

PROPAGATION   Soak pods in water for 12 hours, then sow in beds with a light soil covering. Transplant early to minimize high mortality in beds.

GT   5–10 days
GR   High

USES   The wood is used to make musical instruments, the small branches are used for fuel, and the leaves are good fodder for cattle.

Dalbergia latifolia | FABACEAE

NAMES   Rosewood (c)/ Nookkam (t)/ Kala shisham (h)

LEAF
STYLE Pinnate
ARRANGEMENT Alternate
THORN Absent
LENGTH 3 to 5 cm
WIDTH 1.5 to 5 cm

FLOWER
COLOUR White/Cream
AROMA Yes
SIZE Less than 1 cm

FRUIT
COLOUR Brown/Rusty
SIZE 3 to 5 cm
TYPE Seedpod

DESCRIPTION	A tall deciduous tree growing over 10 metres in height, with smooth bark and no thorns.
HABITAT	This tree enjoys the full sun. It is generally found on hillocks, and occasionally it is found on the plains.
LANDSCAPE INFORMATION	This tree is slow-growing and drought tolerant. Listed as vulnerable on the IUCN Red List.
PROPAGATION	Soak pods in water for 12 hours, then sow in beds with light soil covering. Transplant early to minimize high mortality in beds.
USES	This plant has been used in the treatment of diarrhoea, dysentery and leprosy. The wood is mainly used for making furniture.

GT   5–10 days
GR   High

Chloroxylon swietenia | RUTACEAE

NAMES Satin wood (c)/ Ven porasu (t)/ Bhirra (h)

LEAF		FLOWER		FRUIT	
STYLE Pinnate		**COLOUR** White/Cream		**COLOUR** Brown/Rusty	
ARRANGEMENT Alternate		**AROMA** Yes		**SIZE** 3 to 5 cm	
THORN Absent		**SIZE** Less than 1 cm		**TYPE** Capsule	
LENGTH 1 to 3 cm					
WIDTH 0.5 to 1.5 cm					

DESCRIPTION
: A medium sized deciduous tree growing up to a height of 10 metres, with rough bark and no thorns.

HABITAT
: This tree is generally found on red soil. It is often cut for timber, and is rarely found as mature trees.

LANDSCAPE INFORMATION
: It is drought tolerant and fast growing. Listed as vulnerable on the IUCN Red List.

PROPAGATION
: Clean and sow seeds directly in beds. Seedling aftercare required.

USES
: The leaves have been applied on wounds and for rheumatism. The wood is used for posts and utensils.

GT 10–14 days

GR Medium

Limonia acidissima | RUTACEAE

NAMES Wood apple (c)/ Vila (t)/ Kaith (h)

LEAF
STYLE Pinnate
ARRANGEMENT Alternate
THORN Straight
LENGTH 1 to 3 cm
WIDTH 0.5 to 1.5 cm

FLOWER
COLOUR White/Cream
AROMA Yes
SIZE 1 to 3 cm

FRUIT
COLOUR Grey
SIZE More than 5 cm
TYPE Berry

DESCRIPTION A medium sized deciduous tree growing up to a height of 10 metres, with rough bark and thorns found on young growth.

HABITAT This tree enjoys the full sun. It is often found on tank bunds or in hedgerows, and rarely found in mature evergreen stands.

LANDSCAPE INFORMATION It is a beautiful, slow-growing tree.

PROPAGATION Clean and soak seeds for 12 hours, then sow in beds or trays. Sprinkle with wood ash to stop caterpillars. It requires to be in the sun after transplanting.

GT 10–14 days
GR Medium

USES The fruit and young leaves are edible. It is also used as a rootstock for citrus species.

Sapindus emarginatus | SAPINDACEAE

NAMES Soap nut (c)/ Reetha (H)

LEAF	
STYLE	Pinnate
ARRANGEMENT	Alternate
THORN	Absent
LENGTH	More than 5 cm
WIDTH	1.5 to 5 cm

FLOWER	
COLOUR	White/Cream
AROMA	Yes
SIZE	Less than 1 cm

FRUIT	
COLOUR	Brown/Rusty
SIZE	1 to 3 cm
TYPE	Drupe

DESCRIPTION A medium sized deciduous tree growing up to a height of 10 metres, with rough bark and no thorns.

HABITAT This plant enjoys the full sun. It is generally found in disturbed areas, and rarely found in mature evergreen stands.

LANDSCAPE INFORMATION It is slow-growing and drought tolerant.

PROPAGATION Clean and soak seeds for 12 hours, then sow in beds or trays.

USES The dried fruits are used in shampoo and as a natural washing agent.

GT 14–30 days
GR High

Clausena dentata | RUTACEAE

NAMES Horsewood (c)/ Kaattu karuveppilai (T)

LEAF
STYLE Pinnate
ARRANGEMENT Alternate
THORN Absent
LENGTH 3 to 5 cm
WIDTH 1.5 to 5 cm

FLOWER
COLOUR White/Cream
AROMA Yes
SIZE 1 to 3 cm

FRUIT
COLOUR White
SIZE Less than 1 cm
TYPE Berry

DESCRIPTION	A deciduous shrub, with smooth bark and no thorns.
HABITAT	This shrub can be found in the open, or as a component of the understorey in a mature forest.
LANDSCAPE INFORMATION	It is drought tolerant, and it attracts butterflies.
PROPAGATION	Clean and sow seeds directly in beds. Seedling aftercare required.
USES	The fruit is edible, and the crushed leaves have been used to treat wounds, mouth infections, and general body pains.

GT 10–14 days
GR Medium

Pongamia pinnata | FABACEAE

NAMES Pungan (T)/ Karanj (H)

L E A F	**STYLE** Pinnate		**F L O W E R**	**COLOUR** Pink	**F R U I T**	**COLOUR** Brown/Rusty
	ARRANGEMENT Alternate			**AROMA** Yes		**SIZE** 2 to 5 cm
	THORN Absent			**SIZE** Less than 1 cm		**TYPE** Seedpod
	LENGTH More than 5 cm					
	WIDTH 1.5 to 5 cm					

DESCRIPTION A medium sized deciduous tree growing up to a height of 10 metres, with smooth bark and no thorns.

HABITAT This tree is found mainly near rivers or water bodies, and it is extensively planted in afforestation programmes.

LANDSCAPE INFORMATION It is a coastal species, is relatively fast growing, and is drought tolerant.

PROPAGATION Clean and soak seeds for 12 hours, then sow directly in bags.

USES A decoction made from the leaves has been used to treat diarrhoea. It is cultivated for its oil, which is used as a fuel and as an insect repellent.

GT 7–10 days

GR High

Phyllanthus polyphyllus | PHYLLANTHACEAE

NAMES   Shrub amla (c)/ Sirunelli (T)

LEAF
STYLE Pinnate
ARRANGEMENT Alternate
THORN Absent
LENGTH Less than 0.5 cm
WIDTH Less than 0.5 cm

FLOWER
COLOUR Green
AROMA No
SIZE Less than 1 cm

FRUIT
COLOUR Green
SIZE Less than 1 cm
TYPE Capsule

DESCRIPTION	A small deciduous tree growing up to a height of 6 metres, with smooth bark and no thorns. Also known as *Phyllanthus racemosus*.
HABITAT	This tree enjoys the full sun. It is a component of the deciduous forest type, and it is occasionally found in mature evergreen stands.
LANDSCAPE INFORMATION	This is a fast-growing tree with an interesting bark pattern.
PROPAGATION	Soak seeds overnight then sow in beds.
USES	The leaves and stems have been used to strengthen the body. The plant has anti-inflammatory properties. The bark is a source of tannins.

GT   2 weeks

GR   Medium

Lannea coromandelica | ANACARDIACEAE

NAMES   Indian ash tree (C)/ Odiyan (T)/ Mohin (H)

LEAF			FLOWER			FRUIT	
STYLE Pinnate			**COLOUR** Yellow			**COLOUR** Red	
ARRANGEMENT Alternate			**AROMA** Yes			**SIZE** Less than 1 cm	
THORN Absent			**SIZE** Less than 1 cm			**TYPE** Drupe	
LENGTH More than 5 cm							
WIDTH 1.5 to 5 cm							

DESCRIPTION	A medium sized deciduous tree growing up to a height of 10 metres, with smooth bark and no thorns.
HABITAT	This tree is occasionally found in forest areas, however it is more usually found by the side of the road, on tank bunds, or agricultural edges.
LANDSCAPE INFORMATION	This tree is fast growing, and is good for creating an early canopy.
PROPAGATION	Clean and soak seeds for 12 hours, then sow in beds or trays. Can propagate from cuttings.
USES	A decoction of the bark has been used to treat stomach ache and dysentery. The wood has termite-resistant properties.

GT   1 month

GR   Medium

Spondias pinnata | ANACARDIACEAE

NAMES   Jackal mango (c)/ Pulimaa (T)/ Ambara (H)

LEAF		FLOWER		FRUIT	
STYLE	Pinnate	**COLOUR**	Yellow	**COLOUR**	Yellow
ARRANGEMENT	Alternate	**AROMA**	Yes	**SIZE**	3 to 5 cm
THORN	Absent	**SIZE**	Less than 1 cm	**TYPE**	Drupe
LENGTH	More than 5 cm				
WIDTH	1.5 to 5 cm				

DESCRIPTION	A large, spreading deciduous tree growing over 10 metres in height, with rough bark and no thorns.
HABITAT	This plant enjoys the full sun. It is usually found on the hillocks of disturbed areas. It is rarely found in mature evergreen stands.
LANDSCAPE INFORMATION	It can be used for variety in landscape planting.
PROPAGATION	Leave seeds in a pile, in a damp corner. Once germinated, plant out in bags.
USES	A paste of the ground bark has been used to treat rheumatism. The leaf juice has been used as a treatment for earache.

GT	1 year
GR	Low

Cassia fistula | FABACEAE

NAMES Indian laburnum (c)/ Sarakkondrai (t)/ Amaltas (h)/ Imagination (m)

LEAF
STYLE Pinnate
ARRANGEMENT Alternate
THORN Absent
LENGTH More than 5 cm
WIDTH 1.5 to 5 cm

FLOWER
COLOUR Yellow
AROMA Yes
SIZE 3 to 5 cm

FRUIT
COLOUR Black
SIZE More than 5 cm
TYPE Seedpod

DESCRIPTION   A medium sized deciduous tree growing up to a height of 10 metres, with smooth bark and no thorns.

HABITAT   This tree is occasionally found in forest areas, however it is more usually found by the side of the road, on tank bunds, on agricultural edges.

LANDSCAPE INFORMATION   This tree has beautiful flowers, and is good for park areas.

PROPAGATION   Clean seeds, scratch and soak for 12 hours, then sow directly in bags. Sprinkle with wood ash to stop caterpillars.

USES   The leaf juice has been used for skin diseases and bone fractures.

 GT   10 days
 GR   Medium

Pterocarpus marsupium | FABACEAE

NAMES Indian kino tree (c)/ Vengai (t)/ Vijayasara (h)

LEAF		FLOWER		FRUIT	
STYLE	Pinnate	COLOUR	Yellow	COLOUR	Brown/Rusty
ARRANGEMENT	Alternate	AROMA	Yes	SIZE	More than 5 cm
THORN	Absent	SIZE	1 to 3 cm	TYPE	Seedpod
LENGTH	More than 5 cm				
WIDTH	More than 5 cm				

DESCRIPTION	A tall deciduous tree growing over 10 metres in height, with rough bark and no thorns.
HABITAT	This tree enjoys the full sun. It is generally found on hillocks in mixed forests, and rarely found in mature evergreen stands on the plains.
LANDSCAPE INFORMATION	It is drought tolerant, has beautiful foliage, and is relatively fast growing. Listed as near threatened on the IUCN Red List.
PROPAGATION	Cut wings and soak for 12 hours, then keep moist in a clay pot. Once germinated, sow the seeds directly in bags.
USES	Bark is used for diabetes and the wood is also a valuable timber.

GT 14–30 days
GR Medium

Pterocarpus santalinus | FABACEAE

NAMES Red sanders (C)/ Santhana (T)/ Lalchandan (H)

LEAF	
STYLE	Pinnate
ARRANGEMENT	Alternate
THORN	Absent
LENGTH	More than 5 cm
WIDTH	1.5 to 5 cm

FLOWER	
COLOUR	Yellow
AROMA	Yes
SIZE	1 to 3 cm

FRUIT	
COLOUR	Brown/Rusty
SIZE	3 to 5 cm
TYPE	Seedpod

DESCRIPTION	A tall deciduous tree growing over 10 metres in height, with rough bark and no thorns.
HABITAT	This plant enjoys the full sun. It is found in exposed locations on hillocks.
LANDSCAPE INFORMATION	It is a timber tree with a beautiful form. Listed as near threatened on the IUCN Red List.
PROPAGATION	Cut wings and soak for 12 hours, then keep moist in a clay pot. Once germinated, sow the seed directly in bags.
USES	A paste made from the wood has been used to treat dysentery, diabetes and immune system disorders.

GT 14–30 days
GR Medium

Tamarindus indica | FABACEAE

NAMES Tamarind (c)/ Puliyan (т)/ Imli (н)

LEAF
STYLE Pinnate
ARRANGEMENT Alternate
THORN Absent
LENGTH 1 to 3 cm
WIDTH 0.5 to 1.5 cm

FLOWER
COLOUR Yellow
AROMA Yes
SIZE 1 to 3 cm

FRUIT
COLOUR Brown/Rusty
SIZE More than 5 cm
TYPE Seedpod

DESCRIPTION	A medium sized deciduous tree growing up to a height of 10 metres, with rough bark and no thorns.
HABITAT	This tree is occasionally found in forest areas, however it is more usually found by the side of the road, on tank bunds, or on agricultural edges.
LANDSCAPE INFORMATION	It is slow-growing and drought tolerant.
PROPAGATION	Clean seeds and soak for 24 hours, then sow in beds or trays. Use seeds from ripe fruits.
USES	It is cultivated for its edible fibres in seedpods. Bark paste has been applied externally for eczema.

GT 30 days
GR High

Ormocarpum cochinchinense | FABACEAE

NAMES   South Indian caterpillar bush (c)/ Elumbotti (T)

LEAF		FLOWER		FRUIT	
STYLE	Pinnate	COLOUR	Yellow	COLOUR	Brown/Rusty
ARRANGEMENT	Alternate	AROMA	No	SIZE	3 to 5 cm
THORN	Absent	SIZE	1 to 3 cm	TYPE	Seedpod
LENGTH	1 to 3 cm				
WIDTH	0.5 to 1.5 cm				

DESCRIPTION	A deciduous shrub, with smooth bark and no thorns.
HABITAT	This shrub is found mainly in disturbed areas. It grows in the full sun, and disappears if the canopy closes.
LANDSCAPE INFORMATION	It is drought tolerant but needs to be planted in semi-shade.
PROPAGATION	Clean and soak seeds for 12 hours, then sow directly in bags or beds.
USES	The leaves are considered to be a general tonic.

GT   5–10 days

GR   High

Senna auriculata | FABACEAE

NAMES   Tanner's cassia (C)/ Aavarai (T)/ Tarwar (H)

LEAF
STYLE Pinnate
ARRANGEMENT Alternate
THORN Absent
LENGTH 1 to 3 cm
WIDTH 0.5 to 1.5 cm

FLOWER
COLOUR Yellow
AROMA Yes
SIZE 3 to 5 cm

FRUIT
COLOUR Brown/Rusty
SIZE More than 5 cm
TYPE Seedpod

DESCRIPTION	A deciduous shrub, with smooth bark and no thorns.
HABITAT	A shrub found mainly in disturbed areas, it grows in full sun, disappearing if the canopy closes.
LANDSCAPE INFORMATION	It is drought tolerant and attracts butterflies.
PROPAGATION	Clean and soak seeds for 12 hours, then sow in beds or trays. Don't transplant too late. Sprinkle with wood ash to stop caterpillars. Sun required after transplanting.
USES	The flowers are edible, and the plant has been used for skin diseases, fever and constipation.

GT 5–10 days
GR Medium

Dichrostachys cinerea | FABACEAE

NAMES   Sickle bush (c)/ Vidatheri (T)/ Kheri (H)

LEAF
- **STYLE** Pinnate
- **ARRANGEMENT** Alternate
- **THORN** Straight
- **LENGTH** Less than 1 cm
- **WIDTH** Less than 0.5 cm

FLOWER
- **COLOUR** Pink and yellow
- **AROMA** Yes
- **SIZE** 1 to 3 cm

FRUIT
- **COLOUR** Brown/Rusty
- **SIZE** 3 to 5 cm
- **TYPE** Seedpod

DESCRIPTION	A small deciduous tree growing up to a height of 6 metres, with rough bark and thorns found on young growth.
HABITAT	This plant is found mainly in disturbed areas. It grows in the full sun, disappearing if the canopy closes.
LANDSCAPE INFORMATION	It is fast growing with beautiful flowers, and is good for creating an early canopy.
PROPAGATION	Clean and soak seeds for 12 hours, then sow directly in bags.
USES	The leaves have been used as a treatment for liver and eye diseases, and the bark has been used for headache and toothache.

GT   5–10 days

GR   Very High

Vitex altissima | LAMIACEAE

NAMES Peacock foot tree (C)/ Mayiladi (T)

LEAF		FLOWER		FRUIT	
STYLE Trifoliate		**COLOUR** Blue		**COLOUR** Purple/Blue	
ARRANGEMENT Opposite		**AROMA** Yes		**SIZE** Less than 1 cm	
THORN Absent		**SIZE** Less than 1 cm		**TYPE** Drupe	
LENGTH More than 5 cm					
WIDTH 1.5 to 5 cm					

DESCRIPTION A medium sized deciduous tree growing up to a height of 10 metres, with smooth bark and no thorns.

HABITAT This tree enjoys the full sun. It is mostly found in disturbed areas, and is rarely found in mature evergreen stands.

LANDSCAPE INFORMATION It is drought tolerant, has beautiful foliage, and is relatively fast growing.

PROPAGATION Clean seeds and soak for 12 hours, then sow in beds or trays. Can propagate from cuttings.

GT Up to 6 months

GR Low

USES The wood is a fine timber, and is water resistant. The bark has been used as a treatment for rheumatic swelling.

Vitex leucoxylon | LAMIACEAE

NAMES White wood chaste tree (C)/ Neer nochil (T)/ Nirgundi (H)

LEAF
STYLE 3 to 5 foliolate
ARRANGEMENT Opposite
THORN Absent
LENGTH More than 5 cm
WIDTH 1.5 to 5 cm

FLOWER
COLOUR White/Cream
AROMA Yes
SIZE 1 to 3 cm

FRUIT
COLOUR Black
SIZE 1 to 3 cm
TYPE Drupe

DESCRIPTION A tall deciduous tree growing over 10 metres in height, with smooth bark and no thorns.

HABITAT This tree is normally found next to rivers in forest areas, however it is also present on tank bunds and along canyons.

LANDSCAPE INFORMATION It is fast growing, and is good for creating an early canopy.

PROPAGATION Clean seeds and soak for 12 hours, then sow in beds or trays.

USES The leaf smoke has been used to treat headaches and catarrh. This is a good timber tree.

GT 1–2 months
GR Medium

Vitex negundo | VERBENACEAE

NAMES Chaste tree (c)/ Nochil (т)/ Sindvar (н)

LEAF		FLOWER		FRUIT	
STYLE 3 to 5 foliolate		**COLOUR** Violet/Purple		**COLOUR** Black	
ARRANGEMENT Opposite		**AROMA** Yes		**SIZE** Less than 1 cm	
THORN Absent		**SIZE** Less than 1 cm		**TYPE** Drupe	
LENGTH More than 5 cm					
WIDTH 1.5 to 5 cm					

DESCRIPTION	A deciduous shrub, with smooth bark and no thorns.
HABITAT	This plant is occasionally found in forest areas, however it is more usually found by the side of the road, on tank bunds, or on agricultural edges.
LANDSCAPE INFORMATION	It has lovely foliage, is fast growing, and is good for fencing.
PROPAGATION	Clean seeds and soak for 12 hours, then sow in beds or trays. Can propagate from cuttings.
USES	The leaf smoke is used as an insect repellent. The plant is used for fencing, and the stem is used for making baskets.

GT 1–2 months
GR Medium

Bombax ceiba | MALVACEAE

NAMES
Red silk cotton (C)/ Ilavam (T)/ Semra (H)/
Solid steadfastness in the material consciousness (M)

LEAF
STYLE Digitate
ARRANGEMENT Alternate
THORN Straight
LENGTH More than 10 cm
WIDTH 5 to 10 cm

FLOWER
COLOUR Pink
AROMA Yes
SIZE More than 5 cm

FRUIT
COLOUR Brown/Rusty
SIZE More than 10 cm
TYPE Capsule

DESCRIPTION
A tall deciduous tree growing over 30 metres in height, with rough bark and thorns found on young growth.

HABITAT
This tree is occasionally found in forest areas, however it is more usually found by the side of the road, on tank bunds, or agricultural hedges.

LANDSCAPE INFORMATION
This is a fast-growing tree with beautiful flowers. It is good for creating an early canopy.

PROPAGATION
Soak seeds overnight, then sow in beds.

USES
The gum is used in treating diarrhoea, menorrhagia and dysentery. The fibre is used as a packing material.

GT 2 weeks
GR Medium

Sterculia foetida | MALVACEAE

NAMES Java olive (C)/ Kudiraippidukkan (T)/ Jangli badam (H)

LEAF
STYLE Pinnate
ARRANGEMENT Alternate
THORN Absent
LENGTH More than 5 cm
WIDTH 1.5 to 5 cm

FLOWER
COLOUR Red
AROMA Yes
SIZE 1 to 3 cm

FRUIT
COLOUR Brown/Rusty
SIZE More than 5 cm
TYPE Capsule

DESCRIPTION A tall deciduous tree growing over 10 metres in height, with smooth bark and no thorns.

HABITAT This tree enjoys the full sun. It is found on hillocks, between rock crevices, and it is rarely found in mature evergreen stands.

LANDSCAPE INFORMATION This tall, fast-growing and handsome tree is good for creating an early canopy, however the flowers emit a very unpleasant odour.

PROPAGATION Clean and soak seeds for 12 hours, then sow in beds or trays.

USES The seeds are edible after roasting. The timber is used to make furniture.

GT 30 days
GR High

Balanites roxburghii | ZYGOPHYLLACEAE

NAMES Desert date (C)/ Nanchundan (T)/ Hingot (H)

LEAF	
STYLE	Bifoliolate
ARRANGEMENT	Alternate
THORN	Straight
LENGTH	0.5 to 1.5 cm
WIDTH	0.5 to 1.5 cm

FLOWER	
COLOUR	Green
AROMA	No
SIZE	Less than 1 cm

FRUIT	
COLOUR	Brown/Rusty
SIZE	3 to 5 cm
TYPE	Drupe

DESCRIPTION	A small deciduous tree growing up to a height of 6 metres, with rough bark and thorns.
HABITAT	This tree is found in drier climates, alongside roads, or in forests. It is often associated with areas rich in limestone.
LANDSCAPE INFORMATION	This tree attracts bees. It is slow-growing and drought tolerant.
PROPAGATION	Soak seeds overnight, then sow in bags. Seeds should be sown on surface of soil.
USES	Even with a bitter, sharp taste, the fruit is digestible. The fruits have been used to treat cough, skin diseases and infertility, and the leaves to treat jaundice.

GT 5–10 days

GR Medium

Hardwickia binata | FABACEAE

NAMES   Indian black wood (c)/ Acha (t)/ Anjan (h)

LEAF		FLOWER		FRUIT	
STYLE Bi-foliolate		**COLOUR** Green		**COLOUR** Brown/Rusty	
ARRANGEMENT Alternate		**AROMA** No		**SIZE** More than 5 cm	
THORN Absent		**SIZE** Less than 1 cm		**TYPE** Seedpod	
LENGTH 1.5 to 5 cm					
WIDTH 1.5 to 5 cm					

DESCRIPTION   A medium sized deciduous tree growing up to 10 metres, with rough bark and no thorns.

HABITAT   This tree enjoys the full sun. It is a component of the deciduous forest type, and is generally found in the hills.

LANDSCAPE INFORMATION   It should be planted in the full sun and poor soil. It is relatively fast growing, and is drought tolerant.

PROPAGATION   Clean seeds before soaking overnight, then sow directly in bags. Keep seedlings in the full sun, and don't overwater.

GT   2 weeks

GR   Medium

USES   It is a valuable timber tree, and the leaves are good fodder.

Allophylus cobbe | SAPINDACEAE

NAMES   Mangrove tit berry (c)/ Siruvalli (T)/ Tippani (H)

LEAF		FLOWER		FRUIT	
STYLE Trifoliate		**COLOUR** White/Cream		**COLOUR** Red	
ARRANGEMENT Alternate		**AROMA** No		**SIZE** Less than 1 cm	
THORN Absent		**SIZE** Less than 1 cm		**TYPE** Berry	
LENGTH More than 5 cm					
WIDTH 1.5 to 5 cm					

DESCRIPTION	A deciduous shrub, with smooth bark and no thorns.
HABITAT	This shrub is normally found in the understorey, and only if the canopy has been recently removed is it found in the open sun. It is also found on sandy beaches and in coastal areas.
LANDSCAPE INFORMATION	It is drought tolerant and attracts butterflies.
PROPAGATION	Clean and soak seeds for 12 hours, then sow directly in bags or beds. Can propagate from cuttings.
USES	A decoction made from the roots has been used to treat diarrhoea. The wood is used for boats and small construction projects.

GT   30 days

GR   Medium

Crateva adansonii subsp. odora | CAPPARACEAE

NAMES   Garlic pear tree (C)/ Maavilingam (T)/ Barna (H)/
Work of the enlightened mind (M)

LEAF
STYLE Trifoliate
ARRANGEMENT Alternate
THORN Absent
LENGTH More than 5 cm
WIDTH 1.5 to 5 cm

FLOWER
COLOUR White/Cream
AROMA Yes
SIZE 1 to 3 cm

FRUIT
COLOUR Red
SIZE 3 to 5 cm
TYPE Berry

DESCRIPTION	A medium sized deciduous tree growing up to a height of 10 metres, with smooth bark and no thorns.
HABITAT	This tree enjoys the full sun. It is found in disturbed areas, and as large trees in mature evergreen stands.
LANDSCAPE INFORMATION	It has beautiful flowers, and is good for park areas.
PROPAGATION	Clean seeds and soak for 12 hours, then sow in beds. Sprinkle with wood ash to stop caterpillars.
USES	The wood is used for making toys.

GT   30 days
GR   Medium

Maerua apetala | CAPPARACEAE

LEAF
STYLE	3 to 5 foliolate
ARRANGEMENT	Alternate
THORN	Absent
LENGTH	0.5 to 1.5 cm
WIDTH	0.5 to 1.5 cm

FLOWER
COLOUR	White/Cream
AROMA	No
SIZE	1 to 3 cm

FRUIT
COLOUR	Red
SIZE	1 to 3 cm
TYPE	Berry

DESCRIPTION	A medium sized deciduous tree growing up to a height of 10 metres, with smooth bark and no thorns.
HABITAT	This tree is found only in the southern districts, in temple groves, on tank bunds, or in forest areas.
LANDSCAPE INFORMATION	With its beautiful flowers and lovely foliage, this tree is great as a landscape feature.
PROPAGATION	Soak seeds overnight, then sow in bags. Seedling growth can lag for some months; keep in the shade until vigorous growth occurs.
USES	The leaves have been used to treat nervous disorders and foot pain.

GT 2 weeks

GR Medium

Butea monosperma | FABACEAE

NAMES Flame of the forest (C)/ Murukkan (T)/ Dhak (H)/
Beginning of the supramental realisation (M)

LEAF
STYLE Trifoliate
ARRANGEMENT Alternate
THORN Absent
LENGTH More than 5 cm
WIDTH More than 5 cm

FLOWER
COLOUR Red
AROMA No
SIZE More than 5 cm

FRUIT
COLOUR Brown/Rusty
SIZE More than 5 cm
TYPE Seedpod

DESCRIPTION A medium sized deciduous tree growing up to a height of 10 metres, with smooth bark and no thorns.

HABITAT This tree is occasionally found in forest areas, however it is more usually found by the side of the road, on tank bunds, or on agricultural edges.

LANDSCAPE INFORMATION It has beautiful flowers, and can be used as a garden feature.

PROPAGATION Clean and soak seeds for 12 hours, then sow directly in bags. Insert only half the seed.

USES The leaves pieced together are used as plates.

GT 10 days
GR Very High

Erythrina suberosa | FABACEAE

NAMES   Corky coral tree (C)/ Mul murungu (T)/
Hadua (H)

LEAF	
STYLE	Trifoliate
ARRANGEMENT	Alternate
THORN	Straight
LENGTH	More than 5 cm
WIDTH	More than 5 cm

FLOWER	
COLOUR	Red
AROMA	Yes
SIZE	3 to 5 cm

FRUIT	
COLOUR	Brown/Rusty
SIZE	More than 5 cm
TYPE	Seedpod

DESCRIPTION   A medium sized deciduous tree growing up to a height of 10 metres, with rough bark and thorns found on young growth.

HABITAT   This tree enjoys the full sun. It is a component of the deciduous forest type, and is generally found on the hillocks.

LANDSCAPE INFORMATION   It is a slow-growing and beautiful tree.

PROPAGATION   Soak seeds overnight, then sow in trays with coconut fibre.

USES   A tea of the flowers is drunk for its cooling properties, and for its calming medicinal action. The flowers make an excellent dye.

GT   2 weeks

GR   Medium

Cadaba trifoliata | CAPPARACEAE

NAMES Three-leaf cadaba (C)/ Vizhudhi (T)

LEAF
STYLE Trifoliate
ARRANGEMENT Alternate
THORN Absent
LENGTH More than 5 cm
WIDTH 1.5 to 5 cm

FLOWER
COLOUR Yellow
AROMA No
SIZE More than 5 cm

FRUIT
COLOUR Red
SIZE More than 5 cm
TYPE Berry

DESCRIPTION A deciduous shrub, with smooth bark and no thorns.

HABITAT This shrub is normally found in the understorey of the forest, and only if the canopy has been recently removed will it be found in the open sun.

LANDSCAPE INFORMATION It is drought tolerant, and is a good plant in semi-shade.

PROPAGATION Clean and soak seeds for 12 hours, then sow in beds. Likes sun after transplanting. Can be propagated by cuttings.

USES The leaves have been used to treat eczema, intestinal worms, body pain and beetle stings. The bark has been used as a nervine tonic.

GT 30–60 days
GR Medium

Pleiospermium alatum | RUTACEAE

NAMES Kurundhu mul thazhai (T)

LEAF	STYLE Trifoliate ARRANGEMENT Spiral THORN Straight LENGTH 3 to 5 cm WIDTH 1.5 to 5 cm	**FLOWER** COLOUR White/Cream AROMA Yes SIZE 1 to 3 cm	**FRUIT** COLOUR Green SIZE 2 to 3 cm TYPE Berry

DESCRIPTION A medium sized evergreen tree growing up to a height of 10 metres, with rough bark and thorns found on young growth.

HABITAT Mature specimens are often found in undisturbed forest remnants, however it can also be found in degraded areas in a modified form.

LANDSCAPE INFORMATION This is a beautiful, slow-growing tree.

PROPAGATION Clean and soak seeds for 6 hours, then sow in beds or trays.

USES The leaf and bark have been used as a treatment for rheumatic pains. The wood has timber value.

GT 21–30 days

GR Medium

Walsura trifoliolata | MELIACEAE

NAMES Three-leaf walsura (c)

LEAF
STYLE Trifoliate
ARRANGEMENT Alternate
THORN Absent
LENGTH More than 5 cm
WIDTH 1.5 to 5 cm

FLOWER
COLOUR White/Cream
AROMA No
SIZE Less than 1 cm

FRUIT
COLOUR Yellow
SIZE 1 to 3 cm
TYPE Drupe

DESCRIPTION A medium sized evergreen tree growing up to a height of 10 metres, with rough bark and no thorns.

HABITAT Mature specimens are often found in undisturbed forest remnants, however it can also be found in degraded areas in a modified form.

LANDSCAPE INFORMATION It is drought tolerant, has beautiful foliage, and is relatively fast growing.

PROPAGATION Clean and sow seeds directly in bags or beds.

USES A decoction made from the bark has been used to treat skin diseases.

GT 30 days
GR High

Borassus flabellifer | ARECACEAE

NAMES Palmyra (c)/ Panai (t)/ Taad (h)

LEAF		FLOWER		FRUIT	
STYLE	Palm leaf	**COLOUR**	Green	**COLOUR**	Black
ARRANGEMENT	Whorled	**AROMA**	No	**SIZE**	More than 5 cm
THORN	Straight	**SIZE**	More than 5 cm	**TYPE**	Drupe
LENGTH	More than 5 cm				
WIDTH	More than 5 cm				

DESCRIPTION
An evergreen palm, with rough bark and no thorns.

HABITAT
This palm is occasionally found in forest areas, however it is more usually found by the side of the road, on tank bunds, or on agricultural edges.

LANDSCAPE INFORMATION
This is a beautiful, slow-growing palm.

PROPAGATION
Directly sow seeds in situ; no preparation required.

USES
The leaves are used for thatching, the fruits are edible, and the wood is used for house scaffolding.

GT 1 year

GR Medium

Phoenix pusilla | ARECACEAE

NAMES   Ceylon date palm (C)/ Siru echan (T)/ Palavat (H)

LEAF		FLOWER		FRUIT	
STYLE Palm frond		**COLOUR** Yellow		**COLOUR** Black	
ARRANGEMENT Whorled		**AROMA** Yes		**SIZE** Less than 1 cm	
THORN Straight		**SIZE** Less than 1 cm		**TYPE** Drupe	
LENGTH More than 5 cm					
WIDTH 0.5 to 1.5 cm					

DESCRIPTION	An evergreen palm, with rough bark and thorns found on young growth.
HABITAT	This palm is occasionally found in forest areas, however it is more usually found by the side of the road, on tank bunds, or on agricultural edges.
LANDSCAPE INFORMATION	The fruits attract birds and animals.
PROPAGATION	Clean and soak seeds for 6 hours, then sow in beds or trays.
USES	The fresh juice is cooling and laxative.

GT   1–2 months

GR   Medium

Phoenix sylvestris | ARECACEAE

NAMES Wild date palm (c)/ Pericham (T)/ Khajur (H)

LEAF
STYLE Palm frond
ARRANGEMENT Whorled
THORN Straight
LENGTH More than 5 cm
WIDTH 1.5 to 5 cm

FLOWER
COLOUR Yellow
AROMA Yes
SIZE Less than 1 cm

FRUIT
COLOUR Orange
SIZE 1 to 3 cm
TYPE Drupe

DESCRIPTION An evergreen palm, with rough bark and thorns found on young growth.

HABITAT This palm is occasionally found in forest areas, however it is more usually found by the side of the road, on tank bunds, or on agricultural edges.

LANDSCAPE INFORMATION This is a beautiful, slow-growing palm.

PROPAGATION Clean and soak seeds for 6 hours, then sow in beds or trays.

USES The ripe fruit is edible, and the juice from the tender leaves has been given as a treatment for diarrhoea. The trunk is used in construction, especially for posts.

CT 1-2 months
GR Medium

CEYLON OAK / *Kumbathiri*
Schleichera oleosa

INDEX

SPECIES LIST

A

B

C

D

E

SOURCE CREDITS

22–23 *Crataeva adansonii ssp. odora*, **Dinesh Valke**; 89 *Wrightia tinctoria*, **Rison Thumboor**; 207 *Dichrostachys cinerea*, **Bernard Dupont**; 216 *Crataeva adansonii ssp. odora*, **Dinesh Valke**: WIKIMEDIA COMMONS

44–45 *Memecylon umbellatum*; 66–67 *Madhuca longifolia var. latifolia*; 88 *Barringtonia acutangula*; 110–111 *Ficus benghalensis*; 132–133 *Euphorbia antiquorum*; 154–155 *Cochlospermum religiosum*; 176 *Pongamia pinnata*; 177 *Spondias pinnata*; 200–201 *Butea monosperma*; 226–227 *Schleichera oleosa*: SHUTTERSTOCK

All images courtesy the AUROVILLE BOTANICAL GARDENS unless specified.

Any omissions brought to our notice will be rectified in future editions.

ACKNOWLEDGEMENTS

This book and its wealth of information regarding native trees and their ecosystem is the direct result of over fifty years of dedicated work of restoring and researching forests. Many have contributed to it by giving freely of their deep botanical knowledge. In particular, the contributions of the following deserve to be mentioned by name: Walter Gastmans, Jaap den Hollander, Balachandran N., Neil Meikleham, Santo Nanci and Sivasankaran A.

ABOUT THE AUTHORS

Paul Blanchflower arrived in Auroville in 1991 from the UK, having studied ecology. He expected to stay for two or three years to gain experience with tropical forestry. However, the place offered so many unique opportunities and experiences that he has been based here for the last thirty years.

Since August 2000, he has been in charge of the development of the Auroville Botanical Gardens. This has kept him occupied for the past twenty-three years, building up on 50 acres of bare land an organization that looks after a garden dedicated to the conservation of the Tropical Dry Evergreen Forest. He has been involved in large-scale re-afforestation projects in India and is a founding member of the Ecological Restoration Alliance of India (era-india.org). He currently works closely with the Ramco group, developing environmental projects with them for their companies and CSR programme.

Landscape architect trained in France, **Marie Demont** has spent the last fifteen years in Auroville working with plantation and afforestation projects. As a result of her association with Auroville Botanical Gardens, she is involved in large-scale ecological restoration, with a focal point on threatened native species. Her enthusiasm for nature drives her to photograph and document the ecosystem which emerges in the Auroville bioregion.

HarperCollins *Publishers* India

At HarperCollins India, we believe in telling the best stories and finding the widest readership for our books in every format possible. We started publishing in 1992; a great deal has changed since then, but what has remained constant is the passion with which our authors write their books, the love with which readers receive them, and the sheer joy and excitement that we as publishers feel in being a part of the publishing process.

Over the years, we've had the pleasure of publishing some of the finest writing from the subcontinent and around the world, including several award-winning titles and some of the biggest bestsellers in India's publishing history. But nothing has meant more to us than the fact that millions of people have read the books we published, and that somewhere, a book of ours might have made a difference.

As we look to the future, we go back to that one word—a word which has been a driving force for us all these years.

Read.